PEOPLE AND THEIR ENVIRONMENT

Series editor: Neil Punnett

Resources, Energy and Development

Neil Punnett

Oxford University Press

Oxford University Press, Walton St, Oxford OX2 6DP

Oxford   New York   Toronto
Delhi   Bombay   Calcutta   Madras   Karachi
Petaling Jaya   Singapore   Hong Kong   Tokyo
Nairobi   Dar es Salaam   Cape Town
Melbourne   Auckland

and associated companies in
Berlin   Ibadan

Oxford is a trademark of Oxford University Press

ISBN 0 19 913326 3

Typesetting by Tradespools Ltd., Frome, Somerset

Printed in Hong Kong

Pupil Profile Sheets

A Pupil Profile base sheet is provided which can be copied to provide sheets for each pupil. It is intended that each pupil should receive a profile sheet at the end of each Unit in this book.

At the end of each Unit is an Assessment. The second page of the Assessment contains a box in which the details for the Pupil Profile Sheets are listed. The teacher can transfer the details to the base sheet.

The profile will be completed following discussion between the teacher and pupil. It will therefore provide an agreed record of achievement throughout the course. It is hoped that the profile will help to enhance the learning of pupils, increase motivation, and provide diagnostic information for the teacher.

Contents

Unit 1 The resource system; forestry and fishing 4

1.1 Introduction 4
1.2 A classification of resources 6
1.3 The geography of resources 8
1.4 Forestry 10
1.5 Forestry management 12
1.6 Forestry in Britain 14
1.7 Forestry in the Ivory Coast 16
1.8 Forestry in Brazil 18
1.9 Fishing 20
1.10 Norwegian fishing 22
1.11 Fishing in decline 24
1.12 Fishing policy 26
Assessment 28

Unit 2 Mining 30

2.1 Minerals and mining systems 30
2.2 Tin mining 32
2.3 China clay 34
2.4 Iron ore 36
2.5 Coal 38
2.6 The price of coal 1 40
2.7 The price of coal 2 42
2.8 Oil: a vital resource 44
2.9 Oil in Saudi Arabia 46
2.10 Minerals in Botswana 48
Assessment 50

Unit 3 Energy 52

3.1 World energy demands 52
3.2 Energy in the UK: changing demands 54
3.3 Electricity 56
3.4 Hydro-electricity 58
3.5 Nuclear power 1 60
3.6 Nuclear power 2 62
3.7 Alternatives: tidal power 64
3.8 Alternatives: wind power 66
3.9 Alternatives: solar power 68
3.10 Alternatives: geothermal power 70
3.11 The power game 72
Assessment 74

Unit 4 Water 76

4.1 The hydrological cycle 76
4.2 Water supply 78
4.3 Water from Kielder 80
4.4 Irrigation 82
4.5 A dam nuisance 84
4.6 Navigation 86
4.7 Inland waterways in Britain 88
4.8 Dirty water 90
4.9 Water pollution 92
4.10 A broad conflict 94
Assessment 96

**Unit 5 Primary products from the
        developing world** 98

5.1 Over-dependence 98
5.2 Nigeria's problem 100
5.3 The pattern of world trade 102
5.4 Breaking the chains 104
5.5 Britain and the developing world 106
5.6 Tourism in the developing world 108
Assessment 110

Unit 6 Approaches to development 112

6.1 What is development? 112
6.2 A development index 114
6.3 Economic growth 116
6.4 Aid 118
6.5 UK aid 120
Assessment 122

Index 125
Acknowledgements 126
Photocopiable Pupil Profile base sheet 128

Unit 1: The resource system; forestry and fishing

All the photographs on these two pages show *resources*.

A *natural resource* is something provided by the Earth which can be used by people. It may be a mineral, a plant or an animal. The natural resource may be mined, quarried, harvested, caught or reared.

The work and skill of humans can be called *human resources*. The knowledge and skills of such people as farmers, weavers, steelworkers and computer programmers are all human resources. Some countries have a surplus of human resources, other countries do not have enough. People from Ghana, Burkina Faso and other West African countries work in the Ivory Coast, for example. The Ivory Coast has a high demand for farmworkers.

Countries may lack particular skills: British companies have been forced to import hundreds of computer experts from the USA and West Germany because there were not enough skilled Britons. Britain has to use American and German skills while it trains its own computer experts. In the same way several Middle Eastern countries such as Saudi Arabia and Kuwait have had to import skilled workers from India, Pakistan, Europe and the USA while they train their own people in the new industries created by the oil boom in the Middle East.

Figure A

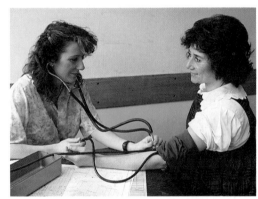

Figure B (*above*)   Figure C (*below*)

Figure D (*above*)

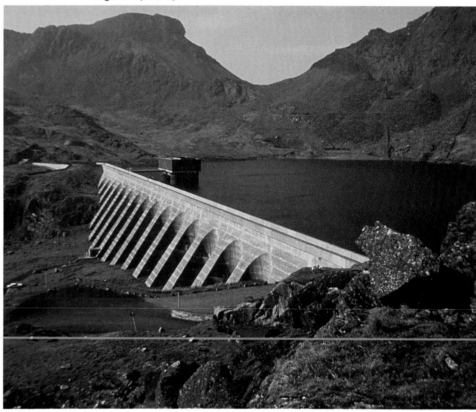

Figure E (*above*)

Figure F (*above*)   Figure G (*below*)

Figure H

QUESTIONS

1 What are (a) natural resources and (b) human resources?

2 Study the photographs and list as many natural and human resources as you can see.

3 a) What is the Ivory Coast's problem with its human resources?
  b) How has the Ivory Coast overcome this problem?

4 How do Britain and Saudi Arabia face problems with their human resources?

5 What problems might be created by importing foreign workers into a country?

5

Natural resources can be divided into two types: *non-renewable* (or finite) resources and *renewable* (or infinite) resources.

Renewable resources are always present. Provided that care is taken not to over-exploit them, renewable resources will not run out and can be used over and over again. Fish provide a good example. With modern fishing methods featuring radar and echo-sounders it is easy for *over-fishing* to occur. Young fish will be caught if nets with a small mesh size are used. This will reduce fish numbers in following years and a vicious circle of decline occurs. It is important to know the 'highest sustainable catch' of a fishing ground.

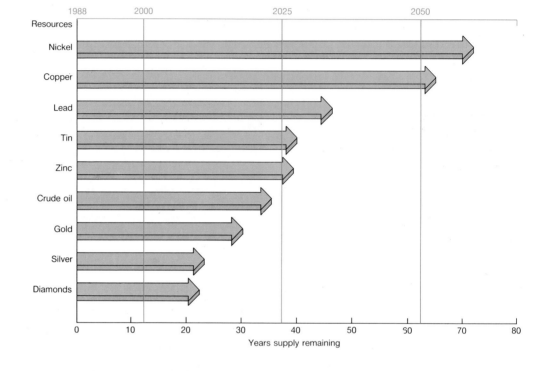

Figure A Number of years supply remaining of certain non-renewable resources at present rates of mining

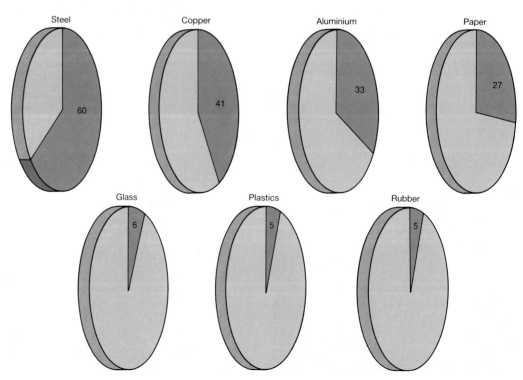

Figure B The percentage of certain resources recycled in the UK, 1986

Non-renewable resources, such as coal, oil, iron ore and other minerals, are in limited supply. Once people have used them they are gone and cannot be replaced. There have been worries about the rate of use of some non-renewable resources. If mining continues at the present rate some vital resources may disappear within a few decades (Figure A). However, fresh discoveries are being made all the time and the known *reserves* are regularly increased.

Some non-renewable resources can be used more than once through *recycling*. Figure C shows a 'bottle bank' where people can place old bottles. The glass is melted down and used again. Over 150 000 tonnes of glass are reclaimed each year from the UK's bottle banks. This represents about 9 per cent of total glass consumption in the UK. In the Netherlands over 50 per cent of the nation's total consumption of glass is recycled.

More recycling could take place. Each year the average British family throws away 50 kg of metal, 40 kg of plastics, and paper equivalent to six trees! Aluminium is easily recyclable, but only a third of the aluminium consumed in the UK is recycled instead of the estimated 80 per cent possible. If a deposit was charged on drink cans much more aluminium would be recycled.

Figure C A bottle bank

QUESTIONS

1 Copy out the table of resources below and indicate which are renewable and which are non-renewable by ticking the correct column:

Renewable and non-renewable resources

Resource	Renewable	Non-renewable
Coal		✓
Timber		
Rock salt		
Water		
Oil		
Sea salt		
Diamonds		
Fish	✓	
Iron ore		
Wheat		

2 How can renewable resources be exhausted? Give an example.

3 a) Study Figure A. Copy and complete the table below showing how many years supply of the listed minerals remain:

World mineral resources

Mineral	Supply remaining (number of years)
Tin	
Copper	
Diamonds	
Gold	30
Zinc	
Lead	
Nickel	
Oil	

   b) Why is it unlikely that the minerals will actually run out in the time stated in the table?

4 Give five examples of natural resources which can be recycled.

5 What are the advantages of recycling?

6 Study Figure B.
   a) Which two resources have the highest amount of recycling?
   b) How could the amount of recycling be increased?

Figure A shows the location of the world's ten major producers of iron ore, one of the most vital mineral resources. **Answer questions 1–3** before reading on.

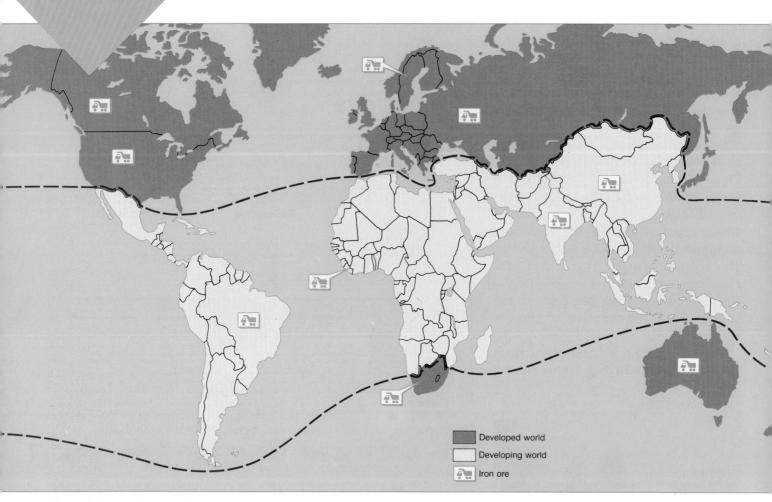

Developed world
Developing world
Iron ore

Figure A The world's ten major producers of iron ore

The developed countries have relied on the developing world to supply them with vital resources such as raw materials for industry. This reliance is increasing rapidly because many of the resources in the developed world are running out. For example, the USA produces only 12 per cent of the world's oil but uses 32 per cent. Such imbalances between amounts produced and amounts consumed causes a flow of resources from the developing world to the developed world. Oil tankers and bulk carriers transport the resources in a continuous shuttle service.

The importance of the resource trade routes to the developed countries was underlined in 1987 when the US, British and French navies sent warships to the Persian Gulf to escort oil tankers through the war zone between Iran and Iraq. A third of the world's oil exports pass through the Persian Gulf.

Crude oil

Country	Production (million tonnes)
USSR	619
USA	516
Saudi Arabia	271
Mexico	138
UK	127
China	122
Iran	89
Venezuela	88
United Arab Emirates	72
Libya	49

Coal

Country	Production (million tonnes)
USA	750
China	736
USSR	484
Poland	192
South Africa	158
India	145
Australia	125
UK	105
West Germany	84
Canada	32

Copper

Country	Production (thousand tonnes)
Chile	1290
USA	1090
USSR	1020
Canada	712
Zambia	565
Zaire	501
Poland	431
Peru	364
Australia	240
Philippines	233

Gold

Country	Production (tonnes)
South Africa	683
USSR	270
Canada	81
USA	72
China	65
Brazil	55
Australia	39
Philippines	34
Colombia	21
Papua New Guinea	18

Tin

Country	Production (thousand tonnes)
Malaysia	41
Indonesia	23
Thailand	22
Brazil	20
Bolivia	20
China	18
USSR	17
Australia	8
UK	5
Peru	3

Figure B The world's top ten producers of certain major resources

Figure C (*left*) US warships escort oil tankers through the Persian Gulf

QUESTIONS

1 Using an atlas to help you, name the ten iron ore producing nations shown on Figure A.

2 On an outline map of the world make a copy of Figure A and add to it symbols to show the location of the five minerals listed in Figure B. Your completed map should show sixty symbols.

3 In which area are most of the major producers of the six resources, the developed world or the developing world?

4 Why are developed countries becoming more reliant upon developing countries for resources?

5 Why were developed countries prepared to send warships to the Persian Gulf in 1987 to protect oil tankers?

Thirty per cent of the earth's land surface is covered by forest (Figure A). Forest is a renewable resource which provides many goods and services for people (Figure B). There are five main types of forest.

Equatorial rain forest

High temperatures and high rainfall throughout the year allow a continuous growing season. The trees are broad-leaved hardwoods such as teak, rosewood and mahogany. There are hundreds of thousands of species of plants and animals within this type of forest. Equatorial rain forest covers about 8 per cent of the earth's land surface but is home for over 40 per cent of the world's species.

Tropical deciduous forest

Found in the monsoon areas of southern Asia and the tropical areas of Africa and South America that have a hot, dry season. Because the canopy is not continuous, sunlight can penetrate and there is often dense undergrowth.

Sub-tropical evergreen (Mediterranean) forest

Made up of trees such as pine and oak, and shrubs such as rosemary, thyme and lavender. The trees are adapted to the summer dry season. They have waxy and leathery leaves to reduce water loss through transpiration. Much of this forest has been cleared in Europe and America.

Figure A The world's forests

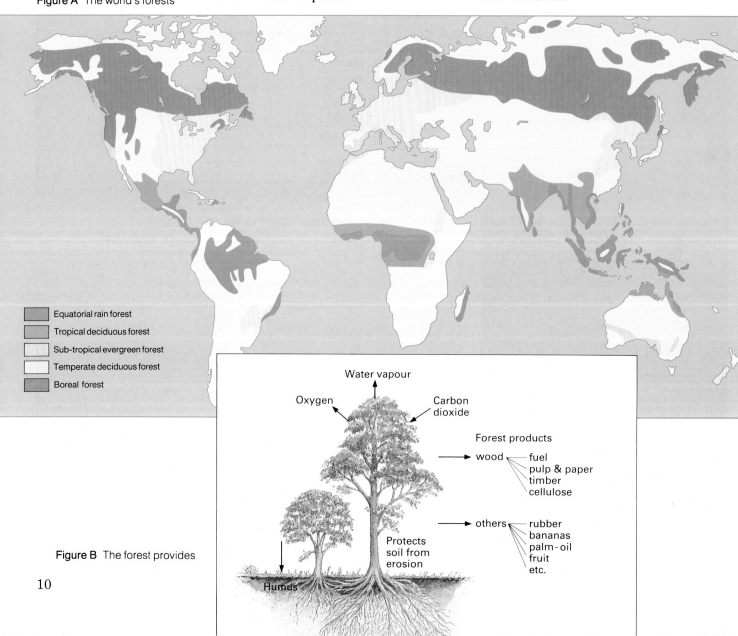

Equatorial rain forest
Tropical deciduous forest
Sub-tropical evergreen forest
Temperate deciduous forest
Boreal forest

Water vapour

Oxygen

Carbon dioxide

Forest products

wood — fuel
pulp & paper
timber
cellulose

others — rubber
bananas
palm-oil
fruit
etc.

Protects soil from erosion

Humus

Figure B The forest provides

Temperate deciduous forest

Contains trees and shrubs including oak, elm, ash and beech. The trees lose their leaves during the cold winters. There are some conifers on poorer soils or at higher altitudes. Much of this forest has been cleared.

Boreal forest

This forms a vast expanse of coniferous evergreen trees, covering 7 per cent of the land's surface. The growing season is short. Pine, spruce, fir and larch are the main species. The trees are slow-growing and shallow rooted because of the frozen sub-soil. Their leaves are needle-like to reduce transpiration and protect against cold. There is only a sparse undergrowth since little sunlight penetrates the forest and the waxy leaves break down very slowly, producing a thin, acid soil. The softwood of the boreal forest is in great demand for timber and paper.

Figure C Coniferous forest, Finland

QUESTIONS

1 What percentage of the earth's land surface is covered by forest?

2 List five forest products.

3 a) Name the five main types of forest.
   b) Using Figure A and your atlas to help you, say what type of forest you would expect to find in the following countries:
   (i) New Zealand (ii) Guatemala (iii) Morocco (iv) Malaysia (v) Canada (vi) Laos (vii) Ecuador (viii) Finland.

4 a) How are trees in Mediterranean areas adapted to the climate?
   b) How are trees in the boreal forest adapted to the climate?

5 a) Copy the world production of timber tables and fill in the missing figures in the 'percentage of world total' columns.
   b) What percentage of the world's coniferous timber is produced by the leading four countries?
   c) What percentage of the world's non-coniferous timber is produced by the leading four countries?
   d) How do you explain the great difference in the two percentages for the four leading countries?

World production of coniferous timber

Country	Timber production (million cubic metres)	Percentage of world total
USSR	296	25
USA	277	23
Canada	129	?
China	111	?
Sweden	45	?
Brazil	37	?
Finland	31	?
Japan	21	1.8
West Germany	21	1.8
Poland	21	1.8
World total	**1187**	**100**

World production of broadleaved, non-coniferous timber

Country	Timber production (million cubic metres)	Percentage of world total
India	214	12.3
USA	158	?
Brazil	153	?
China	121	?
Indonesia	121	?
Nigeria	79	?
USSR	60	3.4
Malaysia	40	2.3
Tanzania	39	2.2
Thailand	37	2.1
World total	**1741**	**100**

1.5 Forestry management

A forest is a renewable resource. Trees can be seen as crops, just like wheat or potatoes. The big difference, of course, is the time that it takes a tree to mature. Different species of tree grow to maturity in different times. The fastest-maturing trees take less than twenty years. Slower-growing trees may take over a century to reach maturity. The climate also affects tree growth. Coniferous trees grow well only if the average daily temperature reaches 9°C.

As the demand grows for timber, fuel, and space for farming, the world's forests become threatened. The great deciduous forests of Europe have all but disappeared as the result of centuries of over-exploitation. Much of Britain would be covered by forest if it were not for the actions of people. Nine per cent of Britain is forested today, but only a small fraction of this is natural forest. The natural forest has been devastated to meet the needs of people. This destruction need not have happened. With careful management the forests could be cropped for ever!

How do you manage a forest? You have to ensure that the trees remain healthy and that a new tree is planted for every tree that is cut down. Caring for the forest can be a complex process (Figure A).

Figure A The timber cycle

1 Seeds are sown and grown in nurseries

2 After two years the seedlings are transplanted in the nursery

3 The area where the trees are to be planted is cleared of any vegetation which might compete with the newly-planted trees for food and light. The area is drained, ploughed and fertilized

4 When the young trees are four years old they are removed from the nursery and planted two metres apart on the ridges of ploughed soil

5 Fences are put up to keep away animals such as deer which might damage or eat the trees

6 Further early fertilizing may be necessary, and the trees are sprayed with pesticides and insecticides

7 After a few years, when the trees are 2 or 3m high, they are thinned (some are cut down) to provide room for the strongest trees to mature. The timber from the thinning is sold, and gardens and parks provide a ready market for small trees

8 After twenty years, when the trees are about 10 m high, they are thinned again. The condition of the soil and the trees is continually checked to make sure they stay healthy

9 After fifty years or more the trees reach maturity and are ready for felling

10 The area is then cleared and made ready for reafforestation

You can see that forestry management is a very patient job. People may work in the forest all their working life and still not see the trees they have planted cut down. It is perhaps more easy to understand why people have not been prepared to invest money in trees which will not earn profits for over fifty years. It is all too easy to take the short-term view, cut down the trees and move on to the next area to be cleared without thinking of the future.

QUESTIONS

1 What factors affect the growth rates of trees?

2 Explain why forest can be called a renewable resource.

3 a) What would be the natural vegetation of much of Britain?
 b) Why is that natural vegetation no longer present?

4 a) What percentage of Britain is forested today?
 b) How much of this is actually natural vegetation?

5 Study Figure A.
 a) Where are the tree seedlings raised?
 b) How old are the trees when they are transplanted into the forest?
 c) How is the area in which they are to be planted prepared for the new trees?
 d) Why is the new forest area fenced?
 e) What does 'thinning' of the forest mean?
 f) When and why is thinning carried out in the forest?

6 a) You are the owner of a small timber company which owns a large area of forest. Your company is short of money. The price of timber has recently risen rapidly. You decide to cut down as much of the forest as you can and not to replant young trees. Write a paragraph giving the reasons for your decision to harvest the forest in this way.
 b) Now change roles. You are a forestry expert living in the area. You hear of the timber company's plans. Write a letter to the owner of the company giving your opinion of the owner's plans and your recommendations as to what the company should do.

1.6 Forestry in Britain

Figure A

The aims of the Forestry Commission

The Forestry Act of 1967 expanded the Forestry Commission's aims to include:

- promoting the interests of forestry
- development of afforestation
- production and supply of timber and other forest products
- production of raw material for industry
- providing employment in rural areas where jobs are scarce
- conserving the natural beauty of the countryside
- providing recreational facilities

Only 9 per cent of Britain is forested. This is one of the lowest figures in Europe (Figure D). Yet woodland is the natural vegetation of most of Britain. Two thousand years ago deciduous trees such as oak, elm, ash and birch covered much of the country. Where did the trees go? They were felled by people to clear the land for farming. The timber was needed for several purposes:

- building
- industrial use
- fuel
- shipbuilding

By 1900 there was little forest left in Britain. The natural landscape had been transformed and the forests had been replaced by fields and moorland. By 1900 only 5 per cent of Britain was forested. Britain's timber needs were met by importing timber, mainly from the colonies of the British Empire.

The First World War (1914–18) placed enormous demands on timber. Imports were reduced by enemy action and Britain's surviving forests were used at an alarming rate. In 1919 the Forestry Commission was set up by the government which aimed to build up a strategic reserve of timber in Britain. The Commission undertook a programme of replanting. They chose coniferous trees such as spruce, larch and pine which grow more quickly than Britain's native deciduous trees. The replanting programme did not meet Britain's growing demands for timber, and the Second World War (1939–45) repeated the problems of the First.

A period of rapid planting followed 1945. The Commission's aims were clear: to reduce Britain's dependence on imported timber and to provide a reserve in case of war. By the late 1950s the threat of nuclear war made such a reserve less important. At the same time there were growing demands for recreation.

The early work of the Forestry Commission was criticized by many people. Dark, dreary conifers were planted in regimented rows with straight boundaries giving the landscape an artificial, geometric appearance. The Commission actively discouraged people from its land. Things improved after 1967 (Figure A).

The Kielder Forest

In Northumberland is Britain's largest forest plantation, Kielder Forest. This area was chosen because forestry was thought to be more profitable than farming. Planting started in 1926 in an area of bleak moorland which supported only poor quality sheep farming and grouse shooting. The thin, infertile peat and boulder clay soils needed specially developed tree planting methods. By the 1980s over 40 000 hectares of land were forested. Planting is almost complete and further expansion is unlikely.

About 50 per cent of the trees are Sitka spruce and another 24 per cent are Norway spruce. The Sitka spruce, from British Columbia, Canada, withstands exposure and poor soil conditions much better than the Norway spruce. Sitka spruce are therefore grown on the higher slopes. Norway spruce is more resistant to the frost which often occurs in the valleys, where the soil is more fertile and the land is less exposed. Scots pine, lodgepole pine and larch are also grown. The light green larch provides a pleasing contrast to the dark green spruce and pine trees.

New roads and houses have been built in the forest. An eventual workforce of 1500 people was forecast and three forestry villages were built at Kielder, Stonehaugh and Byrness. Un-

Figure B The Kielder Forest

Figure C The location of Kielder Forest

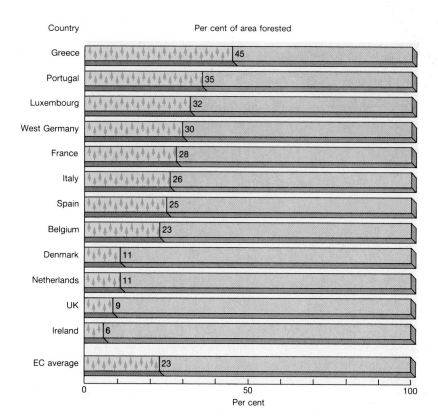

Figure D Percentage of area forested in EC countries

fortunately it was discovered that thinning of the forests led to many of the remaining trees being blown down by the increased wind speeds. Today only about 15 per cent of the forest can actually be thinned; the rest has to be felled together at about 40 to 50 years growth. The average tree at harvest is therefore quite small. This assists the use of machines which, together with the lack of thinning, has reduced the workforce needed in the forests to only 210.

The Commission has provided forest walks, picnic places, viewpoints and car parks for visitors to Kielder. There is an information centre at Kielder Castle. Tea rooms, craft shops and pony-trekking centres are also available.

The produce from Kielder Forest is mainly pulpwood and logs. The pulpwood goes to make paper, packaging and chipboard. The logs are used for construction and pallets. The harvest in the Kielder Forest is over 100 000 tonnes of timber each year. This could reach 500 000 tonnes per year during the next century. Timber is a raw material as versatile as coal or oil; with good management Kielder Forest will be producing timber long after the world's coal and oil have gone forever.

QUESTIONS

1 a) What percentage of Britain is forested?
  b) How does this compare with the year 1900?

2 a) When was the Forestry Commission established?
  b) Why was the Commission established?
  c) Why was the early work of the Commission criticized by some people?
  d) How have the Commission's aims been broadened since 1967?

3 a) Where is Kielder Forest?
  b) Why was Kielder suitable for planting Britain's largest forest?
  c) Explain why two species of spruce tree are grown in Kielder.

4 It was forecast that 1500 people would work in Kielder Forest.
  a) How many actually work there today?
  b) Suggest reasons for this smaller workforce.

5 The table below shows the production of timber in Britain:

British timber production

Year	1960	1965	1970	1975	1980	1985
Production (million cubic metres)	2.5	2.7	3.3	3.8	4.6	4.9

a) Draw a line graph to illustrate these statistics.
b) Explain the pattern revealed by the graph.
c) In 1987 Britain produced only 10 per cent of its timber needs. By the year 2025 it should be producing 20 per cent of its needs. Why would such an improvement be important for Britain?

The Ivory Coast is a large country in West Africa. It has the unhappy distinction of being the country with the highest rate of forest destruction in the world. In 1960 there were 15 million hectares of forest in the Ivory Coast. By 1987 only 1 million hectares were left!

What has caused this disaster?
- commercial timber production
- primitive farming methods
- cutting wood for fuel

Forestry was an important industry for the Ivory Coast. At its peak in 1973, timber made up 35 per cent of total exports and forestry employed 30000 people. Since then the industry has collapsed. Foreign timber companies have pulled out of the Ivory Coast and moved to other African countries where the forests still survive.

How has this human-made disaster been allowed to happen? The timber companies are only interested in the most valuable species of trees in the Ivory Coast's forests. Only a few trees will be cut from each hectare of the forest, but up to a half of the other trees are destroyed in the felling process. The companies cut dirt tracks through previously inaccessible regions of forest. The dirt tracks are used by farmers looking for land.

After choosing a suitable area beside a forest track the farmers cut and burn down the trees to grow cash crops. The Ivorian government provides guaranteed prices and other financial support for farmers, especially for the production of cash crops. Many of the peasants are squatters, living illegally within the forest on land that does not belong to them. The Ivorian

Figure A Giant machines clear the forest

government has banned farming in the remaining forest. Special police units of the country's Forestry Commission do their best to evict squatters, but the damage has usually been done by the time the farmers are discovered.

The Ivory Coast has destroyed what could have been a valuable renewable resource. Mismanagement is to blame. The government should not have allowed the foreign timber companies to destroy so much forest. It should have insisted that the companies replanted trees to replace the ones they took. Yet replanting has been very slow: only 3000 hectares a year during the 1970s. The government felt unable to insist on this because Ivory Coast is a poor country and needs as much money as it can get from timber exports. The short-sightedness of this policy was not apparent to the government until too late.

Reafforestation is expensive. In 1980 a $50 million project was launched with the aid of money from the World Bank and the Commonwealth Development Corporation to replant 20 000 hectares. But this was too little, too late. In 1986 alone 320 000 hectares of forest were felled and only 4700 hectares were replanted.

What effect has the destruction of the forest had on the Ivory Coast?

● A valuable source of income has been lost.

● Vital jobs have been lost.

● Rare species of plants and animals have been lost.

● The risk from bush fires has increased. The forest acted as a fire break. Now the trees have gone the savanna grassland burns every year, threatening farms and people.

● The climate of the Ivory Coast has changed. Rainfall totals have fallen by a third within the last twenty years. This has threatened the country's farms and hydro-electric power stations.

Figure B Timber for export at Abidjan

QUESTIONS

1 Where is the Ivory Coast?

2 What is the Ivory Coast's 'unhappy distinction' in world forestry?

3 How have the following factors contributed to the destruction of the Ivory Coast's forests: (a) commercial timber production, and (b) primitive farming methods?

4 Study the table and answer the questions below.

Forest area in the Ivory Coast

Year	1960	1965	1970	1975	1980	1985
Area (million hectares)	15	13	9	6	3	1.5

a) Draw a line graph to illustrate these statistics.
b) What measures has the Ivory Coast government taken to prevent the deforestation?
c) What more could have been done?
d) Why did the government not do more?

5 Describe the scene in Figure A.

6 How has the loss of the Ivory Coast's forest affected the country?

1.8
Forestry in Brazil

A third of the world's tropical rain forest is in Brazil. Deforestation has become a major issue in Brazil for two reasons:

● the role of Western banks in financing projects which have caused the destruction of vast areas of forest;

● the threat to the Amazon Indians posed by the forest clearance.

POLONOROESTE

In 1981 the Brazilian government set up the North-West Brazil Development Programme (POLONOROESTE) to administer the development of the states of Rondonia and Acre (Figure A). A loan had been arranged with the World Bank to pave the BR364 road through Rondonia to Porto Velho. This action led to a stream of migrants from the South and North-East regions of Brazil.

Most of the migrants are farm labourers seeking their own land in the new frontier region. The government gave landless families free plots of virgin forest, up to 40 hectares each, along the BR364 and its feeder roads. The government has been accused of encouraging migration to reduce social conflict elsewhere in Brazil, regardless of whether the land was suited to the type of farming which the new settlers intended to practice.

The settlers cut and burnt the forest. The smoke from the fires was so dense that aircraft had to be grounded for several days. Once the trees had gone, the settlers planted maize, melons, rice and, especially, coffee. Very soon there were problems:

● strong winds blew away the top soil

● rainwater drained quickly through the sandy soil, leaving plants dry and withered

● water draining through the soil carried vital minerals and nutrients deep down, below the plant roots. This is called leaching

● removal of the trees allowed tropical diseases such as malaria to increase

The result in many areas was disaster. The crops failed to grow and the settlers became ill. Many were forced to abandon their land within two years. Yet still the migrants came. It was estimated that 180 000 moved into Rondonia in 1986 alone. This is far more than POLONOROESTE planned, and far more than Rondonia could cope with. Even the planned settlements lacked services.

Large-scale cattle ranching proved just as disastrous as smallholder farming. Demand for beef from the developed world has encouraged the destruction of the rain forest, but the area is totally unsuited to cattle ranching. The cost of weeding the pasture is higher than the income from beef!

Satellite photographs show that 15 per cent of Rondonia had been de-

Figure A Brazil's forest area and POLONOROESTE

forested by 1987. Some experts maintain that over 80 per cent of the state's forests will have gone by the year 2000.

The agreement with the World Bank, which financed much of the cost of POLONOROESTE, stated that reserves should be created for the Indian peoples. There were thought to be up to 8000 in the region, many of whom had no contact with the outside world. The reserves were set up, but the government has allowed them to be ignored. Mining companies, ranching companies and smallholders have all moved into the Indian reserves. Roads were even planned to go right through the reserves. There have been clashes with the Indians, resulting in deaths on both sides. Many Indians have died from diseases brought in by the settlers. Others have abandoned their traditional life-style and resorted to begging or stealing.

Many people in the USA and Europe protested that their money was being used, through the World Bank, to finance the destruction of the rain forest and the Amazon Indians. The pressure on the World Bank became so great that in 1985 it stopped payments for a while until the Brazilians agreed to safeguard the Indians.

In 1986 the BR364 was extended again, from Porto Velho to Rio Branco in Acre. The same process happened. Migrants streamed in. The forest burned. The Indian reserves were invaded. The settlers struggled and suffered. The paving of the road was funded by the Inter-American Development Bank based in the USA. The Brazilian government ignored the agreements to protect the rain forest and the Indians. Protests resulted in the IDB cutting off the money in 1987.

POLONOROESTE is only one programme, in one part of the Amazon rain forest. Much deforestation is happening elsewhere. A priceless resource is being squandered for short-term profit, mainly financed by the West and mainly to meet the demands of the West for timber, beef and minerals.

Figure B The rain forest burns

QUESTIONS

1 What is POLONOROESTE?

2 What part has the BR364 played in the deforestation of Rondonia?

3 a) Where did the migrants settle in Rondonia?
   b) How did they farm their land?
   c) What was the result of their farming methods?

4 Study the table and answer the questions below.

The increase in deforestation in Rondonia

Year	Total deforested area (sq km)	Percentage of total area of Rondonia
1980	9600	4.0
1981	10450	4.3
1982	11200	4.6
1983	12100	5.0
1984	17330	7.1
1985	25250	10.4
1986	34200	14.1

   a) Draw a line graph to illustrate these statistics.
   b) The paved BR364 was opened in 1984. What effect did this have on the deforestation of Rondonia?
   c) What estimate has been made for the area deforested by the year 2000?

5 a) What effect has POLONOROESTE had upon the Amazon Indians?
   b) How have the World Bank and the Inter-American Development Bank reacted to criticism of the development programme?

6 a) What are the reasons for the POLONOROESTE programme?
   b) Do you think that the destruction of the rain forest and of the Amazon Indians will continue? Why?

1.9 Fishing

Figure A shows the crew of a fishing boat unloading their catch. Fish form only about 2 per cent of human food consumption, but they are a vital source of protein. Over 15 per cent of our protein intake comes from fish. Fish also provide a range of vitamins, oils and minerals. Fishmeal is an important animal feed and fertilizer.

Figure A

Four main groups of sea creatures are caught by the world's fishermen:

1 Pelagic fish live near the surface of the sea. Herring, mackerel, capelin and anchovy are examples. They are mainly used for fishmeal and fish oil. Tuna and salmon are examples of higher value pelagic fish. Over 30 million tonnes of pelagic fish are caught throughout the world each year.

2 Demersal fish live on or near the sea-bed. Cod, haddock, sole and plaice are examples. The world catch of demersal fish is over 20 million tonnes per year.

3 Shellfish (or crustaceans) such as lobster, crab and shrimp fetch high prices. The world catch amounts to three million tonnes per year.

4 Cephalopods such as octopus and squid. About one million tonnes are caught worldwide.

Pelagic fish are caught by several methods. One of the most important is

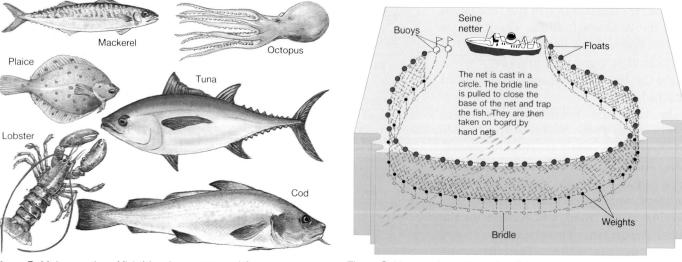

Figure B Major species of fish (drawings not to scale)

Figure C How a seine-net catches fish

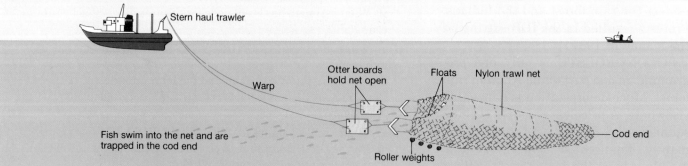

Figure D How a trawl-net catches fish

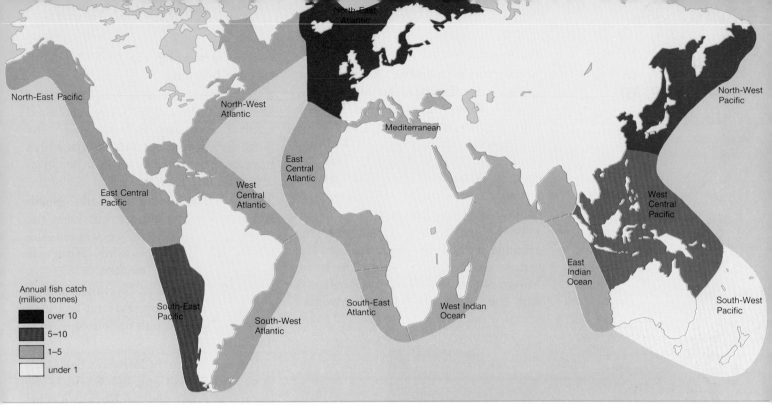

Annual fish catch (million tonnes)
- over 10
- 5–10
- 1–5
- under 1

North-East Pacific

North-East Atlantic

North-West Atlantic

Mediterranean

East Central Atlantic

West Central Atlantic

East Central Pacific

North-West Pacific

West Central Pacific

East Indian Ocean

South-East Pacific

South-West Atlantic

South-East Atlantic

West Indian Ocean

South-West Pacific

seining (Figure C). In some areas, especially developing countries, hand nets may be used to catch pelagic fish. Demersal fish are caught by trawling (Figure D) or by lining, in which baited hooks are used on lines up to a kilometre long trailed by vessels. Shellfish are normally caught by using baskets containing bait. The baskets, often wicker, are lowered into shallow waters and left for a day or two before being retrieved.

The major fishing grounds (Figure E) are in the shallow waters of the continental shelves rather than the deeper waters of the oceans. The shallower waters provide more plankton (the tiny organisms which most fish eat). The plankton need light, and mineral salts which can be obtained from rivers flowing into the sea and from upwellings of water.

The table shows the world's major fishing nations. In recent years several developing countries such as Chile, India and South Korea have built up large fishing fleets. The catch of some traditional fishing nations such as Britain and West Germany has declined in recent years (see pages 24–27) as their fleets have been excluded from the fishing grounds of other nations.

Figure E (*above*) The world's major fishing grounds

Figure F The world's major fishing nations

Country	Fish catch (million tonnes)	Country	Fish catch (million tonnes)
Japan	11.3	South Korea	2.4
USSR	9.8	Thailand	2.3
China	5.2	Indonesia	2.1
USA	4.1	Denmark	1.9
Chile	4.0	Philippines	1.8
Norway	2.8	**World total**	**75.0**
India	2.5		

QUESTIONS

1 Why are fish an important part of the human diet?

2 What are (a) pelagic and (b) demersal fish? Give examples of each.

3 How are pelagic fish caught?

4 How are demersal fish caught?

5 Study Figure E.
   a) Name the world's two major fishing grounds.
   b) Name a fishing ground where the annual catch is:
      (i) between 5 and 10 million tonnes
      (ii) between 1 and 5 million tonnes
      (iii) under 1 million tonnes.
   c) Why are the deep oceans not important fishing grounds?

6 a) Draw a bar graph to illustrate the statistics in the table.
   b) What percentage of the world total is caught by (i) Japan (ii) the twelve nations listed in the table, together?

1.10 Norwegian fishing

The trawler shown in Figure A is part of Norway's massive fishing fleet. Norway is Europe's leading fishing nation. Almost a quarter of Western Europe's fish catch is caught by Norwegian vessels. Norway has only 4 million people, so it is remarkable that the country is such an important fishing nation. There are several reasons to explain this:

1 There are important fish breeding grounds off the Norwegian coast. The waters are rich in plankton. The warm waters of the North Atlantic Drift mix with the cold waters of the Norwegian current providing the ideal temperature for breeding.

2 Norway has a very long coastline, over 20 000 km. There are sheltered natural harbours called fjords. The fjords are deep glaciated valleys which have been drowned by a rise in sea level after the last ice age.

3 The warm waters of the North Atlantic Drift ocean current keep the Norwegian coast free of ice, whereas the Swedish coast at the same latitude is ice-bound for many months.

4 Only 3 per cent of Norway's land is suitable for farming. Fishing has long provided an alternative source of food and income.

Ninety per cent of Norway's fish catch is exported. Fish and fish products account for 6 per cent of Norway's total export earnings. Figure C shows the main species of fish caught. Capelin is the main source of fish oil and fishmeal, which is a fertilizer and animal feed. Some cod is also converted into fish oil, but most of it is frozen and sold as fish fillet. There are a dozen new freezing plants in the north at such places as Hammerfest and Tromso. Part of the cod catch is still dried (stockfish) or salted (klipfish) and exported to West Africa, South America and Mediterranean countries where people have few domestic freezers. They also have large Roman Catholic populations for whom eating fish is a religious practice.

Sixteen thousand Norwegians are full-time fishermen and twice as many fish part-time. In some coastal areas, especially in the north, fishing provides almost the only means of earning a living.

The overall Norwegian fish catch has fallen by 30 per cent over the last twenty years. The resource is under strain. The effects of *over-fishing* first became apparent with the herring catch. Until the 1960s herring made up 70 per cent of Norway's catch. Such vast numbers were caught that the herring population rapidly declined. There were claims of a mysterious disease killing

Figure A (*photograph*) Fishing near Honningsvag, northern Norway

Figure B (*map*) Norway's main fishing grounds and ports

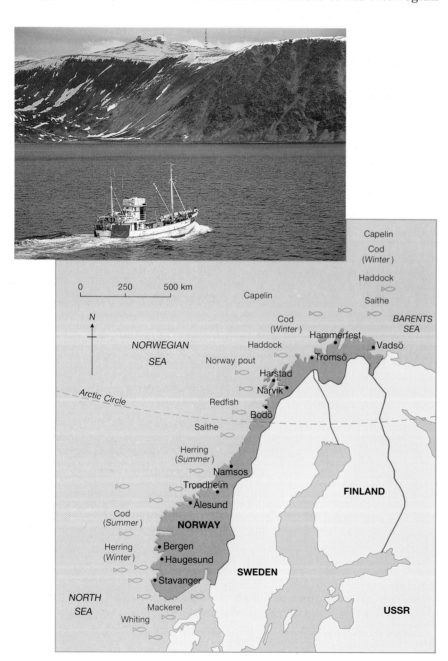

22

the herring, but the real culprit was probably over-fishing. A total ban was imposed on North Sea herring fishing between 1977 and 1983. By 1986 the Norwegian herring catch had reached over 250 000 tonnes, 11 per cent of the total catch. It is unlikely that the herring will return to their previous high levels.

It seems that the lesson of the herring has not been learnt. In the late 1980s the capelin catch declined, again due to over-fishing, this time in the Barents Sea. The Norwegian government has taken steps to protect the fishing industry. A 320 km Exclusive Economic Zone has been declared around the Norwegian coast within which fishing by foreign nations is strictly controlled.

One way to ensure that the fish catch does not decline is to farm the fish rather than hunt them. Over the last decade there has been a rapid development in fish farming, mainly of Atlantic salmon and trout. There are nearly a thousand fish farms in Norway. By 1987 fish farm production of salmon and trout reached 60 000 tonnes, much of which is exported. Some of the fish is flown in refrigerated containers to distant markets such as Japan and the USA. The creation of fish farming has allowed greater control over the resource and fish farming seems destined to take a much larger part of Norway's overall fish production in the future.

Figure D Fish farming has become an important activity

QUESTIONS

1 Why are there important fish breeding grounds off the Norwegian coast?

2 What are fjords and how do they assist fishing in Norway?

3 Why are Norway's fishing ports not frozen in by ice during the winter?

4 a) Study Figure C and estimate the percentages of Norway's catch in 1985 of the following species of fish:
  (i) capelin (ii) cod (iii) Norway pout (iv) herring.
  b) What are the main uses of (i) capelin and (ii) cod?

5 Why is fishing especially important in northern Norway?

6 a) How does Norway's fishing industry provide examples of the misuse of a renewable resource?
  b) What steps have been taken to protect Norway's fishing industry?

7 a) Describe the development of fish farming in Norway.
  b) What advantages does fish farming have over traditional fishing methods?

8 Study the table below:

Norwegian fish exports

Export commodity	Percentage of total fish export value
Frozen fish	37
Salted, dried or smoked fish	24
Fresh fish	2
Fishmeal and fish oil	18
Canned fish	5
Others	14

a) Construct a pie graph to illustrate the statistics in this table.
b) Only 10 per cent of the Norwegian fish catch is sold in Norway. Explain the importance of fish exports to Norway.

Figure C Main species of fish caught, Norway 1985

Species	Catch (thousand tonnes)
Capelin	641
Cod	244
Whiting	233
Saithe	202
Norway pout	114
Herring	253
Mackerel	116
Haddock	25
Others	242
Total	**2070**

Figure A An Icelandic gunboat hits a British frigate as she tries to cut the warps (ropes attached to the trawl-net) of the trawler in the background

1976. British frigates and Icelandic gunboats clash in the icy waters of the North Atlantic. This is the 'Cod War'. Few shots were fired and there were no serious casualties, but Britain's defeat spelt disaster for the British deep sea fishing industry.

Iceland declared a 320 km limit around its shores within which no foreign trawlers were allowed. The Icelandic fishing grounds were the most important fishing areas for the British deep sea trawler fleet. Britain refused to accept the new Icelandic limit and British trawlers continued to fish within the limit. Gunboats of the Icelandic Coast Guard cut the trawl nets and arrested several ships. There were collisions between gunboats and British frigates sent to protect the trawlers. Finally Britain had to accept defeat. British trawlers were also barred from their other traditional fishing grounds in the Norwegian Sea and around Bear Island and Spitzbergen by Norway's Exclusive Economic Zone (page 22).

After 1976 the British deep sea fishing fleet was ruined. The trawlers had been based at four main ports: Grimsby, Aberdeen, Fleetwood and Hull.

Change in the Humber fishing industry

Grimsby and Hull landed a third of the total British fish catch in the early 1970s. By 1987 they handled only 4 per cent. The number of large trawlers in the two ports had fallen from over 100 in 1974 to only two in 1987. In 1974 there were 2200 fishermen in Grimsby; by 1987 there were only 520 left, working on inshore vessels. The loss of jobs in Hull was even greater.

In 1974, 280 000 tonnes of fish were landed at Grimsby and Hull; by 1986 the ports handled 180 000 tonnes. But over 80 per cent of this was brought in by road and much of the rest was landed by foreign vessels. The fish is processed by Humberside's fish processing factories which employ over 9000 people. There are fishmeal and fish oil factories. Famous names such as Bird's Eye, Findus and Ross produce fish fillet, fish fingers, cod steaks, cod fries and many other fish products. Increasingly they are producing other food products on Humberside, including pizza, beefburgers and frozen vegetables.

Britain may well never again have a large deep sea fishing fleet, but it does remain an important fishing nation. There has been growth in the inshore fishing fleet. At Grimsby, for example, there are now 130 inshore vessels, twice as many as in 1974. The inshore vessels catch plaice, halibut, sole and shellfish. Britain's leading fishing ports are now those of Scotland and South-West England. They concentrate on inshore fishing. Mackerel is the most important fish. In the summer, mackerel shoals swim off western Scotland but by the autumn they are found off South-West England. The fishing fleet moves with the shoals.

Shellfish are of increasing importance. They have a high value and are in great demand. Crabs and lobsters are plentiful around the coast of South-West England, oysters are plentiful off east and South-East England, and cockles and whelks are found in shallow bays such as the Wash and Morecambe Bay.

Figure B St. Andrew's Dock, Hull: busy with trawlers in the 1960s (*above*), but filled-in and ready for redevelopment by 1987 (*above right*)

Figure C Fish landed at major British fishing ports, 1986

Port	Fish landed (thousand tonnes)
Ullapool	121.0
Peterhead	119.3
Aberdeen	54.8
Fraserburgh	40.1
Grimsby	31.5
Hull	21.5
Ayr	14.6
Lowestoft	10.2
Newlyn	7.6
North Shields	7.3
Brixham	6.5
Plymouth	3.3
Falmouth	1.1

Figure D UK total fish catch

Year	Fish catch (thousand tonnes)
1950	1220
1960	1045
1970	1100
1980	847
1986	717

QUESTIONS

1 a) What was the Cod War?
   b) What was the cause of the Cod War?

2 Where were the main deep sea fishing ports?

3 Using an outline map of Britain and an atlas to help you:
   a) Mark on the map the locations of the ports shown in Figure C.
   b) Draw bars on the map proportional to the tonnage of fish landed at each port. Let 1 cm represent 20 000 tonnes.

4 Study the table below:

Size and number of vessels in the UK fishing fleet

Length of vessel	Number of vessels		Percentage change
	1976	1982	
under 12 metres	4307	4485	+4.1
12–25 metres	2087	2073	−0.7
25–33 metres	107	120	+?
35–42 metres	135	86	−?
over 42 metres	104	32	−?

   a) Copy the table and complete the column showing percentage change.
   b) What is the pattern of change revealed by the table?
   c) What is the cause of this pattern of change?

5 Study the figures in Figure D.

   a) Draw a line graph to illustrate these statistics.
   b) Explain the changes shown by the graph.
   c) How has the nature of the British fishing industry changed since the 1970s?

6 a) How have the Humber fishing ports been affected by the decline of the deep sea fishing industry?
   b) Why do you think the fish processing industry has continued on Humberside despite the loss of the deep sea catch?

Fishing is a major industry. It is an international issue since fish do not recognize human boundaries. The world's fish stocks are a renewable resource, but effective policies are needed to avoid over-fishing. Figure A shows how the world's total fish catch grew rapidly between 1950 and 1970, but has remained at approximately the same level since.

The nations of the European Community (EC) agreed to a Common Fisheries Policy (CFP) in 1983. Negotiations first began in 1966. The CFP aims to conserve and manage the fish stocks in EC waters. It does this through the following:

1 Total Allowable Catches (TACs) are set. These are agreed annually for all species threatened by over-fishing. The amounts set for the North Sea in 1987 are shown in the table (opposite page). The TACs are then divided into quotas for each member state.

2 A minimum mesh size for fishing nets is set in order to prevent the catching of young fish.

3 Fishing is banned in certain breeding grounds.

4 Compensation is paid if fish prices fall below a 'withdrawal price' which the EC sets each year. The EC also subsidizes freezing of the unwanted fish until demand picks up again.

The CFP also provides money to help restructure the fishing industry. These measures include *decommissioning grants* to help remove uneconomic vessels from the fishing fleet, *laying up grants* for short-term removal from fishing, and *vessel building and modernization grants*.

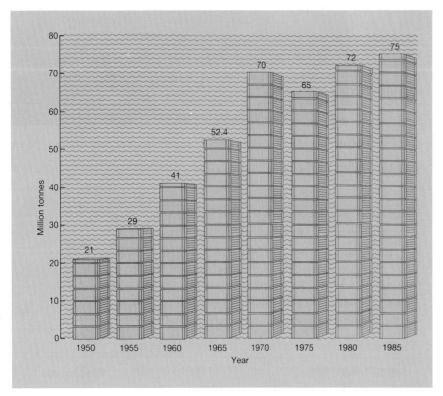

Figure A (*above*) The world's total fish catch, 1950–85

Figure B One of Britain's Fisheries Patrol Dornier aircraft monitoring the fishing grounds – the bans and quotas of the CFP need careful policing

The United Nations Law of the Sea

Until the 1960s the world's oceans were seen as common property, open to all nations. This was 'the freedom of the high seas'. Countries with coastlines controlled 5 or 20 km 'territorial waters' around their shores. In the 1960s this traditional system began to break down. Two developments threatened to destroy the system:

● several nations declared 320 km Exclusive Economic Zones (EEZs) around their coasts;

● some developed countries were using advanced technology in fishing and oil production which was allowing them to take a large slice of the oceans' wealth.

The United Nations set up the Third Law of the Sea Conference in 1973. It was intended to develop a treaty which would make the seas truly international, controlled by the United Nations. After ten years the Conference produced a treaty which set up an International Seabed Authority to control the deep ocean beds and develop their resources for the benefit of all nations. Although most of the world's nations have signed the treaty, few have actually agreed to ratify it. Some nations have rejected it, including Britain and the USA. Britain objects to sharing its sea-bed mining experience with the rest of the world.

The UN Law of the Sea accepts the 320 km EEZ as the best way of controlling and conserving fish resources from over-fishing. National governments are given the responsibility. The Law of the Sea also covers shipping, scientific research and marine pollution. It cannot operate until 60 nations ratify the treaty – and this seems a long way off.

QUESTIONS

1 a) Describe the pattern of the world's total fish catch between 1950 and 1985 from Figure A.
b) Explain the pattern you have described.

2 What do the following abbreviations represent:
(a) CFP (b) TAC (c) EEZ?

3 How does the CFP help the European Community's fishing industry?

4 Study the table below:

TACs set by the CFP for certain fish species in 1987

Fish species	TAC for 1987 (thousand tonnes)	Percentage change from 1986
Mackerel	372	+11
Plaice	149.5	−16
Haddock	129.5	−34
Cod	116.5	−28
Whiting	101.5	0
Saithe	96	−20
Sole	11	−45
Total	**976**	**−12**

a) Name the two fish species which did not have their TAC reduced.
b) Why did the other five species have their TAC reduced by the CFP?
c) How do you think the TACs will be enforced?

5 a) Why was the UN Third Law of the Sea Conference set up in 1973?
b) What does the Law of the Sea treaty do?
c) Why has Britain refused to sign the treaty?

6 It is 1976. The Cod War is at its height.
a) You are a representative of Iceland's Department of Fisheries. Write a letter to the British Government stating your case for a 320 km EEZ.
b) Now change roles. You are a member of the British Ministry of Agriculture, Forestry and Fisheries. Write a letter in reply to the Icelandic letter stating Britain's case for continuing to fish in Icelandic waters.

Unit 1 ASSESSMENT

In the first three questions five possible answers are given. Choose the best answer in each case:

1 What percentage of the area of Britain is forested:
   A 28 per cent   B 9 per cent   C 72 per cent
   D 2 per cent   E 33 per cent?   (1 mark)

2 Pelagic fish are:
   A tiny creatures which provide the main food for larger fish
   B fish which live on or near the sea-bed
   C fish with hard shells
   D fish which live near the surface of the sea
   E creatures such as octopus and squid.   (1 mark)

3 The most important fishing nation in Western Europe is:
   A Iceland
   B The UK
   C Denmark
   D West Germany
   E Norway   (1 mark)

4 'Trees can be seen as crops, just like wheat or potatoes.'
   a) How are trees similar to crops like wheat and potatoes?   (2 marks)
   b) What is the big difference?   (1 mark)

5 Study the table below:

Forested area in Britain

Year	Percentage of land forested
1087	65(estimate)
1900	5
1987	9

   a) (i) What happened to the forests of Britain between 1087 and 1900?   (1 mark)
      (ii) What was the timber used for?   (3 marks)
   b) What has been the main cause of the increase in the area of Britain forested by 1987?   (2 marks)
   c) Referring to a specific example of a forest plantation in Britain:
      (i) Draw a simple sketch map to show its location.   (4 marks)
      (ii) Describe and explain its development and exploitation.   (8 marks)

Questions 6–9 refer to Figure A.

6 a) What was the total area of forest in Brazil in 1987?   (1 mark)
   b) What is meant by 'productive' and 'unproductive' forest?   (2 marks)
   c) How much of the total area of forest is productive?   (1 mark)
   d) How much of the productive area has been logged?   (1 mark)

7 Large areas of Brazilian forest are being felled.
   a) Describe and explain *two* benefits of this to the local people.   (4 marks)
   b) Describe and explain *two* benefits of this to developed countries.   (4 marks)

8 What problems are created by the widespread felling of forest in Brazil?   (5 marks)

9 'Wherever we live, our hands are on the chainsaws which are destroying the tropical rain forest.' Explain this statement.   (4 marks)

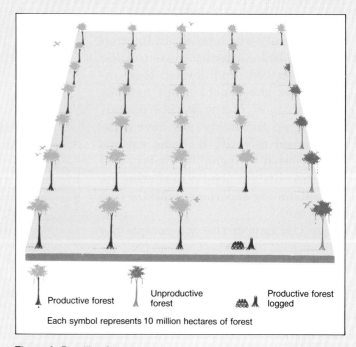

Productive forest   Unproductive forest   Productive forest logged

Each symbol represents 10 million hectares of forest

Figure A Brazilian forests

10 Why is the North Sea an important fishing ground?
(6 marks)

11 The graph (Figure B) shows the tonnage of fish unloaded by UK trawlers at Hull docks.
  a) What was the tonnage in 1976? (1 mark)
  b) What was the tonnage in 1986? (1 mark)
  c) Explain why the decline occurred. (6 marks)

TOTAL: 60 marks

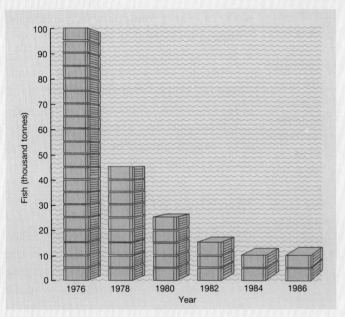

Figure B The tonnage of fish landed by UK trawlers at Hull, 1976–86

Details for pupil profile sheet Unit 1

Knowledge and understanding

1 Resource
2 Natural resource
3 Human resource
4 Renewable resource
5 Non-renewable resource
6 Over-exploitation of resources
7 Recycling
8 Forestry management
9 Over-fishing
10 Fishery management

Skills

1 Written description from a photograph
2 Interpreting pie graphs
3 Use an atlas to find countries
4 Use an atlas to find natural vegetation regions
5 Calculating percentages
6 Role play
7 Draw a line graph
8 Draw a bar graph
9 Draw a pie graph
10 Draw proportional bars on a map

Values

1 Awareness of need to manage the world's resources carefully
2 Awareness of contrasting attitudes to conservation measures

Unit 2: Mining

Within the earth's crust are substances called minerals. Minerals may consist of a single element, such as copper and sulphur, but most are a compound of elements. Limestone, for example, is a compound of calcite, quartz and clay. Coal, oil and gas are often called minerals, but strictly speaking minerals are inorganic (containing nothing derived from living things).

People have used rocks and minerals since earliest times. At first, flint and other rocks which break with a sharp edge were used as tools and weapons. Some minerals were used for ornaments and decoration. Later, clay was used to make pottery and metals were used for tools and weapons.

In normal rocks, minerals occur only in small amounts. Geological processes can concentrate minerals into *veins* which may be large enough to be mined. Rocks containing such veins are called *ores*.

Figure A Copperware, Nigeria (*top*), trading emeralds on the street, Colombia (*middle*), and a silver ingot (*bottom*)

How minerals are formed

Most of the main ores are the result of igneous activity. For example, lead, zinc, tin, silver and copper are deposited from hot liquids rising from igneous intrusions within the earth's crust. Igneous gases may also deposit minerals. Some minerals such as gypsum, salt and potash can be formed by the evaporation of sea water.

Sedimentary processes can help to concentrate minerals, including sand, gravel, clays, peat, coal and oil. Weathering can create new minerals such as bauxite which is formed by the breakdown of aluminium silicate rocks under wet tropical conditions. Kaolin is formed from the weathering of granite.

Mining

There are nearly three thousand minerals, but only a few dozen are of use to people. They can be divided into a number of groups according to their use:

● for metal production, for example, iron ore, bauxite, tin, copper and zinc

● for jewellery, ornaments and bullion production, for example, gold, silver, diamond, ruby, emerald and jade

● for chemical production, for example, sulphur, mercury, potash and gypsum

● for construction, for example, limestone, granite, slate and clay

Methods of mining

Open-cast mining, or quarrying, takes place where the mineral is near the surface. The soil and any overlying rock, called the overburden, is stripped away by mechanical excavators. This is a cheap form of mining.

Adit mining involves a simple tunnel along the mineral vein, usually on a hillside.

Drift mining involves driving a tunnel at a shallow angle into the ground. This allows a railway to run down to the mineral.

Shaft mining involves cutting a vertical shaft down to underground mineral veins. Technological progress has allowed mine shafts to be cut much deeper into the earth's crust. The world's deepest mines are in South Africa where gold mines have been sunk over 3 kilometres underground. At such great depths the rock temperature reaches 50°C. Refrigerated air has to be pumped down the mine through a second shaft.

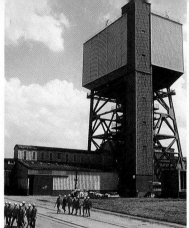

Figure B Three types of mine: a drift mine (*above left*), an open-cast mine (*centre*), and a shaft mine (*far right*)

Dredging of minerals from sea and river waters. Sand, gravel, gold and tin are mined in this way. There is increasing interest in the deposits of minerals in nodules on the ocean floor. The nodules contain manganese, plus copper, nickel and cobalt. This may be an important source of minerals in the future.

The success of mining depends upon a number of factors:

● The quality of the ore. High-grade ores will be more profitable than low-grade ores.

● The amount of ore present. Larger deposits will be cheaper to mine per unit.

● The mining conditions. If the mineral is near the surface and in large veins it will be cheap to mine. Veins can be thin, or shattered by faulting.

● The accessibility of the mine. If the ore cannot be transported to market it is useless. The more accessible ores are mined first.

● The market for the mineral. Prices for the mineral may vary. A rise in price may lead to the development of smaller, less accessible, or low-grade deposits. A fall in price may lead to the closure of such mines. A fall in world tin prices in 1986/87 caused the closure of several Cornish tin mines. They could not compete with the large river-dredged deposits of Malaysia.

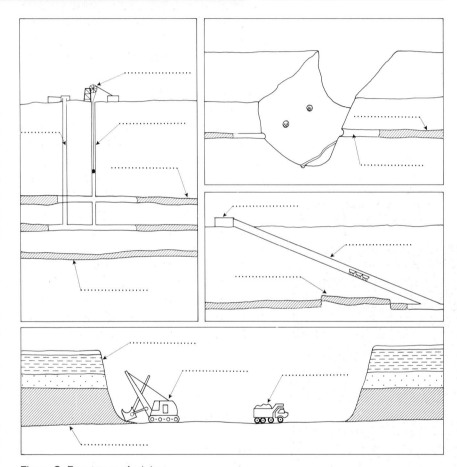

Figure C Four types of mining

QUESTIONS

1 a) What is a mineral?
b) Give four uses of minerals.

2 What are (a) mineral veins and (b) ores?

3 How may the following processes form minerals:
(a) igneous activity (b) sedimentation (c) evaporation of sea water (d) weathering?

4 Copy the four drawings (Figure C) and add suitable labels at the arrows describing the method of mining shown by each.

5 How can the success of a mine be affected by (a) the accessibility of the mine (b) the market for the mineral?

Bronze, pewter, solder and tin plate are all products made from the soft white metal called tin. Tin ore is usually found in veins, called lodes, in rocks, mainly granite. Tin is also obtained from alluvial ores, that is, ores which have been washed away and deposited by rivers.

Tin occurring in lodes is extracted by mining. Alluvial ores are extracted by dredging or by gravel pumping. Dredging is usually much cheaper than mining, so areas with alluvial ores can obtain tin more cheaply. This difference in the economics of the two mining methods has had very important effects upon the tin producing nations.

Figure A A Cornish tin mine

Tin mining in the UK

During the early nineteenth century most of the world's tin was produced from mines in Cornwall. Maximum output was reached in 1871 when 11 000 tonnes of tin were extracted from over 100 mines. The Cornish industry collapsed during the 1890s when tin began to be mined in Bolivia and the Far East. Cornish tin could not compete with the cheaper imports. Between 1920 and 1970 only two small tin mines

survived in Cornwall, producing less than 2000 tonnes a year.

In 1971 the Wheal Jane tin mine was opened. It was soon followed by three more. Cornish production reached over 5000 tonnes by 1984. The revival in production was due to:

● the rapid rise in tin prices during the 1970s

● improved production methods which allowed Cornwall's low-grade ores to be more cheaply processed

● government grants to encourage industry to move to Cornwall, an area of high unemployment

By 1984 there were two thousand jobs in six Cornish tin mines. Then disaster struck. The world price of tin had been kept at around £8500 a tonne by the International Tin Council. In October 1985 the ITC abandoned its price support operations because demand for tin had fallen. The result was a collapse in the price to less than £3500 a tonne. Cornish tin cost at least £6500 a tonne to mine. Four mines closed. One thousand three hundred miners' jobs were lost. Wheal Jane and South Crofty were saved only at the last moment by government aid. Tin mining in the UK faces an uncertain future unless world prices rise again.

What caused the fall in demand for tin? The decline of the steel industry throughout the world has reduced the demand for tin plate. And changes in technology have affected the demand for tin. Most cans are now made from aluminium rather than tin plate. Less solder is used for electrical connections. Pewter has fallen out of fashion as a material.

Tin mining in Malaysia

Malaysia's tin occurs in vast alluvial deposits as well as in underground lodes. Giant barges dredge the tin from lakes and rivers and separate it from waste.

In 1905 there were nearly a quarter of a million tin workers in Malaysia.

Figure B Tin in Cornwall

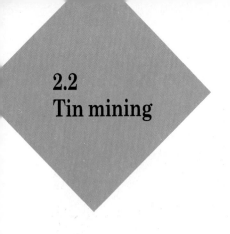

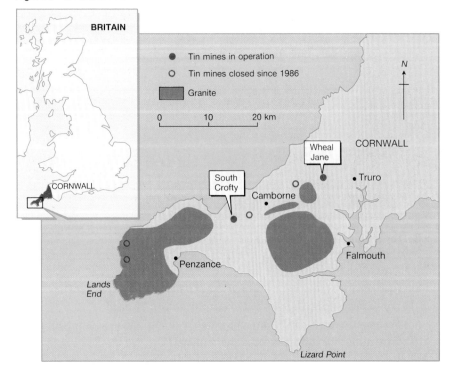

Dredges were introduced in the 1920s, cutting the workforce by two-thirds. Malaysian tin production averaged 60 000 tonnes per year during the 1970s. There were 625 quarries using high pressure hoses and 45 dredges employing 30 000 people. The quarries produced tin at £4500 per tonne. The dredges were cheaper at £3500 per tonne.

The collapse of world tin prices in 1985, which almost destroyed the UK tin industry, also badly hit Malaysia. Half of the dredges and quarries lay idle. Eighteen thousand jobs were lost, leaving only 12 000 workers. Malaysian tin production slumped to 29 135 tonnes in 1986. The Malaysian government was unable to support its tin industry in the way that the UK did because of lack of money. Despite the cutbacks, Malaysia's tin industry will survive, however, because of its lower production costs. The same cannot be said for Bolivia.

The deep mines in the Andes have some of the most difficult mining conditions in the world. Average production costs in Bolivia are over £8000 per tonne. After 1985 the Bolivian tin industry collapsed. The tin mining workforce fell from 50 000 to less than 9000; only a few low-cost mines survived. Many of the unemployed tin workers were forced to turn to crime or to dealing in the illegal drug, cocaine. What future is there for Bolivia's tin industry?

Figure D A Malaysian tin dredge at work

Figure C Striking Bolivian tin miners on a protest march

QUESTIONS

1 Name the two ways in which tin occurs and describe how each one is mined.

2 Study the table below:

Production of tin in the UK

Year	1800	1871	1900	1910	1950
Output (tonnes)	2500	11000	6900	4850	910
Year	1960	1970	1980	1984	1986
Output (tonnes)	1300	1700	3300	5050	2850

a) Draw a bar graph to illustrate these statistics.
b) Explain the pattern revealed by the graph.

3 a) In 1985 the price of tin was £8500 per tonne. In 1986 the price had fallen to only £3500 per tonne. What caused the sharp fall in the price of tin?
b) What effects did the decline in tin prices have upon the tin industries in (i) the UK (ii) Malaysia (iii) Bolivia?

4 a) Copy and complete the table below:

Average cost of producing one tonne of tin

Country	Average cost per tonne (£)
Bolivia	8000+
UK	?
Malaysia quarried	?
dredged	?

b) Account for the different costs of producing tin in the three countries.
c) What effect does this have upon the economic viability of tin mining in these three countries?

2.3 China clay

A china tea service, paint, paper, tiles, cosmetics, animal feed, polish, fertilizer, medicines... what do they have in common? The answer is kaolin, also known as china clay. Kaolin is one of Britain's most important mineral products.

Kaolin is a white, powdery clay. It is found in granite areas. Kaolin formed millions of years ago when the granite was broken down by hot, acid gases and fluids that rose from deep within the earth's crust. Granite consists of three minerals: feldspar, mica and quartz. As the granite decomposed the feldspar changed into kaolin, leaving the mica and quartz unaffected.

Kaolin is found in many places throughout the world. However, it is often stained and mixed with impurities. High-quality kaolin is rare. The two most important areas of high-quality kaolin are Georgia in the USA and Devon and Cornwall in England.

Figure A shows the two main areas where china clay is found in England, near St. Austell in Cornwall and at Lee Moor near Plymouth in Devon. Production began over two hundred years ago, on a small scale at first. By 1900 annual production reached half a million tonnes. There was little further growth until after the Second World War. The introduction of new technology and the opening of new mines has allowed production to increase to nearly four million tonnes a year by 1987.

Figure B A monitor at work

The kaolin lies beneath an *overburden* of soil which is removed by excavators. The kaolin is then quarried with the aid of a remote-controlled hose, or monitor (Figure B), which squirts a high pressure jet of water at the rock face. The heavier quartz sand and mica is washed to the bottom of the pit leaving the finer clay and water to run away into tanks where the clay settles at the bottom (Figure C). Impurities are removed and the clay is pressed and dried. In the blending plant, computers are used to produce a blend of kaolin to the right specification.

The clay is then packed into lorries or railway trucks and is distributed. Kaolin forms the major part of the trade of the ports of Par and Fowey (Figure A). To reduce road congestion and nuisance, the owners, English China Clays (ECC), have built a lorry road to Fowey along the course of an old railway line.

The landscape around the kaolin mines is scarred by the tall, white spoil heaps consisting of the sand washed out from the clay by the monitors. Streams in the area run white because of the waste material. For each tonne of kaolin over five tonnes of sand has to be removed. Some of the sand is used in road building, or concrete production, but most is tipped to form the glistening white hills.

Some Cornish people frown on the pollution, but most accept it. Cornwall is an area of very high unemployment (21 per cent in 1987), and kaolin provides the largest single source of work (ECC employs over 6000 people).

Figure A The china clay industry of South-West England

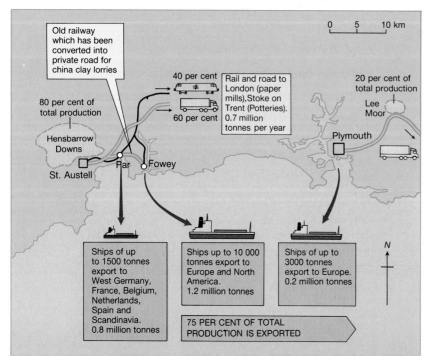

0   5   10 km

Old railway which has been converted into private road for china clay lorries

40 per cent

Rail and road to London (paper mills), Stoke on Trent (Potteries). 0.7 million tonnes per year

60 per cent

80 per cent of total production

20 per cent of total production

Lee Moor

Hensbarrow Downs

Plymouth

St. Austell

Par   Fowey

N

Ships of up to 1500 tonnes export to West Germany, France, Belgium, Netherlands, Spain and Scandinavia. 0.8 million tonnes

Ships up to 10 000 tonnes export to Europe and North America. 1.2 million tonnes

Ships of up to 3000 tonnes export to Europe. 0.2 million tonnes

75 PER CENT OF TOTAL PRODUCTION IS EXPORTED

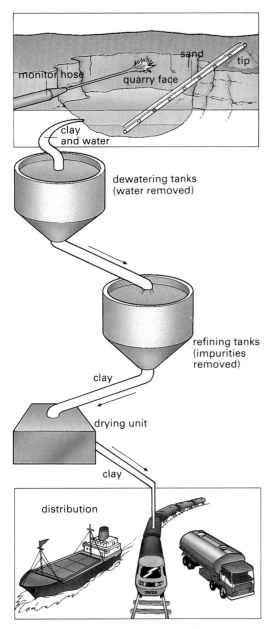

Figure E Loading china clay for export at Fowey

Figure C (*above*) The production process of Kaolin

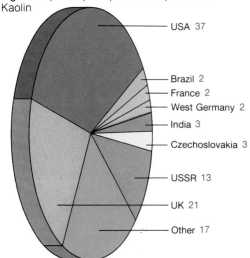

Figure D The world's major producers of Kaolin (percentage share of production)

Labels on Figure C:
- monitor hose
- sand
- quarry face
- tip
- clay and water
- dewatering tanks (water removed)
- refining tanks (impurities removed)
- clay
- drying unit
- clay
- distribution

Labels on Figure D:
- USA 37
- Brazil 2
- France 2
- West Germany 2
- India 3
- Czechoslovakia 3
- USSR 13
- UK 21
- Other 17

QUESTIONS

1 a) What is kaolin, and how is it formed?
b) What are the main uses of kaolin?

2 a) Where is kaolin found in Britain?
b) Which British area is most important?
c) What was the total production of kaolin in Britain in 1987?

3 a) What percentage of British kaolin production is exported?
b) Which three sea ports handle the export of kaolin?

4 a) What percentage of world kaolin is produced in Britain?
b) Name the other two major producers of kaolin.

5 English China Clays want to open a large new kaolin mine near St. Austell in Cornwall, on the edge of the Cornwall Area of Outstanding Natural Beauty. A Public Enquiry is to be held.

a) Form a group of four people. Choose one of the following roles:
► A representative of the Council for the Protection of Rural England.
► A representative of English China Clays.
► An official representing the kaolin miners' trade union.
► A member of the St. Austell Shopowners' Association.

b) Decide what the views of the person you represent will be. Write down those views and the reasons for them.
c) Each person presenting evidence at the Public Enquiry has to provide an illustrated pamphlet of their views. Fold a piece of plain A4 paper into three pieces and design a pamphlet featuring the following:
   (i) a map of the mining area of St. Austell and the surrounding area
   (ii) a short history of kaolin mining in the area
   (iii) a summary of the uses of kaolin
   (iv) a description of the environmental problems associated with kaolin mining
   (v) a summary of the views and reasons you listed in part (b).
d) Each group member should present their views on the proposal for mining kaolin to the group. Discuss each view and then vote on whether the proposal should be allowed to proceed.

6 a) What are your personal views on the pollution and environmental damage done by kaolin mining?
b) Do you think that more should be done to protect the environment around the kaolin mines? If so, who should pay for it?

One of the most vital materials for modern industry is steel. Iron ore is the raw material for steel. Iron ore is the term given to rocks which contain iron. High-grade ores may contain over 60 per cent iron. Low-grade, or lean, ores may contain under 30 per cent iron. Britain was once a major producer of iron ore, but the ores were lean and expensive to use. Britain now imports almost all the iron ore used in its steelworks.

High-grade iron ore is a valuable resource. Even very remote places can be profitable provided the ore is of high enough quality. Inaccessible places such as the Amazon Basin in Brazil and the frozen lands of Labrador in Canada are important centres for iron ore production. Another example is found in the orefields of the southern Sahara Desert in Mauritania, West Africa.

Mauritania

In the north of Mauritania is a range of hills which contain high-quality iron ore, over 65 per cent iron content. The Mauritanians did not have the money or the machines to exploit their iron ore. They allowed it to be developed by a group, or consortium, of companies from the developed world, with the aid of the French government (Mauritania had previously been a French colony).

Iron ore mines were opened at Zouerate in the 1960s. A new town , F'Derik, grew out of the desert to reach a population of 8000. The iron ore is mined in vast open-cast mines (like quarries) such as the one shown in Figure B. The iron ore is transported by rail along Mauritania's first and only railway to the port of Nouadhibou where a large ore terminal has been built (Figure C). The 625 km long railway was very expensive to build. It includes a long tunnel and needed complex foundations where the track crosses moving belts of sand dunes.

Figure A Mauritania

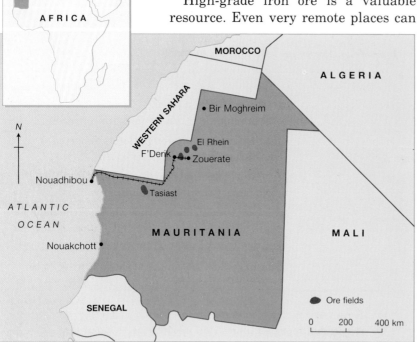

Figure B Mining iron ore in the Sahara Desert, Mauritania

Figure C The iron ore terminal at Nouadhibou

By 1973 Mauritania was producing 7 million tonnes of iron ore a year. The ore made up 93 per cent of the country's export earnings. In 1974 the Mauritanian government *nationalized* the ore industry (that is, it took over the whole development and paid compensation to the consortium). The Mauritanians then hoped that they could earn money from their ore rather than seeing the profit going to foreign companies.

In 1984 production began from a new orefield at El Rhein, 40 km north of Zouerate. There are vast reserves of ore here, but it is of low quality, only 37 per cent iron content. Annual output from El Rhein will rise to 6 million tonnes. It is estimated that the Zouerate iron ore reserves will be exhausted by 1995. In the same year a second phase of the El Rhein orefield should go into action to raise annual ore production to 15 million tonnes.

Mauritania has spent some of the money earned from ore exports on building up other industries so that it will not be so dependent upon iron ore – this is called *diversifying* the economy. By 1986 iron ore made up only 40 per cent of total exports. Nearly 60 per cent was provided by fish and fish products.

The waters off Mauritania are one of the richest fishing grounds around Africa, providing an annual catch of 600 000 tonnes. The waters were exploited mainly by foreign vessels until 1980 when a 370 km Economic Exclusion Zone was declared. A new fishing fleet has been built and a new deepwater port at Nouakchott was opened in 1986. By 1986 55 000 tonnes of fish were caught by Mauritanian vessels and fish exports were valued at £170 million compared with only £6 million in 1979. Fish freezing and processing plants have been built at Nouadhibou, together with a small oil refinery.

Perhaps most significant of all is the construction of a small electric arc steelworks at Nouadhibou. This will use a little of the country's iron ore. Mauritania would earn much more money and have more jobs for its people

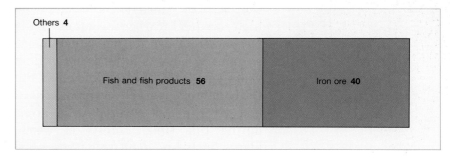

Figure D Mauritania's exports (by value), 1986

if it could export steel rather than ore. However, most of the ore is still exported. The money Mauritania earns from ore sales is used to pay for the import of manufactured goods from the developed world. Some of these have been made from Mauritanian iron ore!

QUESTIONS

1 a) What is iron ore?
b) What is meant by (i) high-grade and (ii) low-grade iron ore?

2 a) Where is Mauritania?
b) Where are Mauritania's iron ore fields?

3 Why did Mauritania allow a consortium of foreign companies to develop its iron ore?

4 Study Figure B.
a) Describe the scene in the photograph.
b) What is this type of mine called?

5 a) How is Mauritania's iron ore exported?
b) Why was the export route expensive?

6 Study Figure A.
a) Describe the route of the Zouerate–Nouadhibou railway.
b) Why do you think the railway was not built in a straight line between the two places?

7 a) Figure D shows Mauritania's export earnings in 1986. What percentage of the total was earnt by iron ore?
b) Use the figures below to draw a divided bar similar to that in Figure D. Draw your bar 100 mm long and let 1 mm represent 1 per cent.

Export earnings of Mauritania in 1983

Commodity	Percentage of total export earnings
Fish and fish products	48
Iron ore	51
Others	1

c) Compare the two bars. Describe and explain the differences between the two.

8 a) Why is it important that Mauritania diversifies its economy?
b) How has the government tried to do this?

Coal is a rock which burns because of its high organic (carbon) content. It is formed from wood and other plant remains. Coal was formed 300 million years ago during a time known as the Carboniferous period. Swamps, lakes and river deltas covered wide areas during this time. Forests of woody plants, including giant tree ferns, grew beside the waters. When the plants died they did not decay because they were buried in the mud. Slowly the plant matter turned into peat.

The peat was buried by more mud on which new swamp forests grew. The peat was compressed by the increasing layers of mud. Over millions of years, pressure and heat turned the peat slowly into lignite, a soft, crumbly brown coal. Lignite burns with a smoky flame. Further compression turned the lignite into true coal.

This black rock has had a dramatic effect upon the human race. It was the fuel of the Industrial Revolution in Europe which marked the start of our modern industrial world. Coal was the fuel to power the steam engines which operated the new factory machines. Coal was used to heat the factories. Coalfields became the sites of vast industrial areas. Small villages grew into bustling, smoky cities. The Ruhr in West Germany is a good example of this kind of development.

Figure A A modern coal-mine at Gelsenkirchen

Figure B The Ruhr coalfield (inset: cross-section of the coalfield)

Coal-mining in the Ruhr

The Ruhr region was mainly farmland until the 1820s. Then coal began to be mined on a large scale. Coal seams were exposed at the surface in the valley of the River Ruhr (Figure B). The earliest mines were drifts or adits cut horizontally into the valley sides. Soon there were hundreds of mines throughout the area of the *exposed coalfield*.

The coal seams dip northwards from the Ruhr Valley and are soon covered by other rocks. This area is called the *concealed coalfield*. By the early 1840s, shaft mines were sunk down to the concealed coalfield. Mining continued to spread rapidly northwards as deeper shafts were sunk.

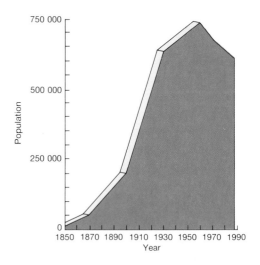

Figure C The population of Essen, 1850–1988

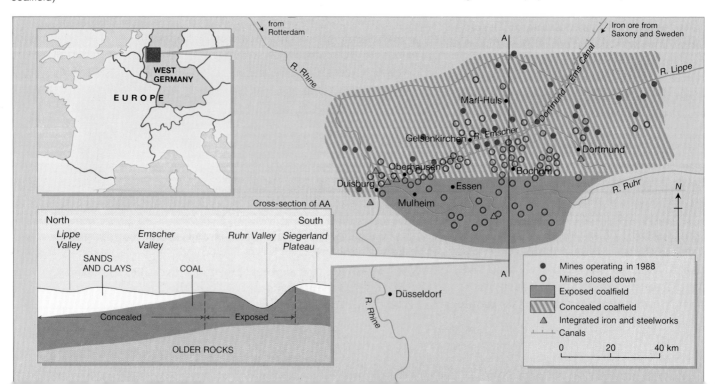

Ruhr coal was especially valuable since over two-thirds of it was coking coal. The coking coal plus the ironstone found within the coal measures ('blackband iron ore') encouraged the growth of iron and steel making. Coal and steel led an economic boom. Small towns grew into sprawling industrial cities within a few years. The industrial growth was greatly helped by the Rhine waterway and a network of canals which made transport of bulky raw materials and products cheap and easy.

For over a hundred years the Ruhr's coal-mines operated at full production, but since the 1950s the situation has changed. The long period of growth slowed and then stopped. By the late 1950s the Ruhr's coal industry was in decline (Figure D).

What has caused this dramatic change in fortune?

● Demand for coal dropped in the face of strong competition from cheap imports of oil and gas. Homes and industry moved away from coal to these cleaner, cheaper and easier fuels.

● The vast open-cast coal-mines of Australia, South Africa and the USA can provide coal much more cheaply than the Ruhr's shaft mines. Several German coal users have turned to such cheaper imports.

● The decline in the steel industry, one of the Ruhr's major coal customers, has reduced demand for coking coal.

● Increased automation has reduced labour demands.

The decline in the coal industry would have been even greater were it not for the money provided by the West German government in subsidies. In 1987 this amounted to a staggering £3340 million. Plans were introduced to reduce the workforce by a further 30 000 and cut production from 58 million tonnes to 50 million tonnes by 1990. The decline of the Ruhr's coal industry is proving as rapid as its earlier growth.

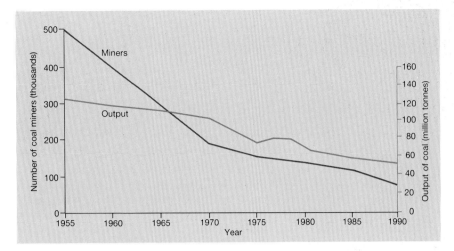

Figure D (*above*) Declining output and employment in the Ruhr coal industry

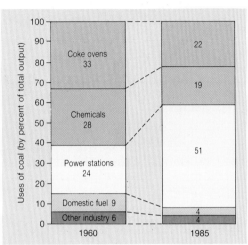

Figure E The changing uses of Ruhr coal

QUESTIONS

1 a) What is coal?
 b) When was coal formed?
 c) How was coal formed?

2 a) Where were the earliest coal-mines in the Ruhr?
 b) What sort of mines were they?

3 Explain the difference between an exposed and concealed coalfield.

4 Why did Ruhr coal encourage the development of an iron and steel industry?

5 Study Figure C.
 a) What was the population of Essen in
  (i) 1850 (ii) 1870 (iii) 1900 (iv) 1930?
 b) What explains the growth of Essen's population?

6 Study Figure D.
 a) How many miners were there in the Ruhr in (i) 1955 (ii) 1970?
 b) How many miners were there predicted to be in 1990?
 c) What was the output of coal in (i) 1955 (ii) 1970?
 d) What was the predicted output for 1990?

7 Why has the Ruhr's coal industry declined since the 1950s?

Figure A Church Enstone

Consideration

Study Figure A. Describe the view shown in the photograph. Choose five words from the list below which you think could be applied to this landscape:

peaceful	attractive
industrial	ugly
rural	urban
noisy	agricultural
polluted	unpolluted

Figure A is a view of the countryside in north Oxfordshire in central England. This is the area on which the following simulation is based. A large coalfield has actually been discovered here, but it is too deep to mine economically at present. Nevertheless, a time may come when the imaginary events in this simulation become reality.

1 Form a group of four. Each group member must take on the role of a person attending the Public Enquiry which is considering a proposal from British Coal to build three mines in Oxfordshire. The roles are to be taken in alphabetical order of your surnames:

▶ A representative of British Coal.
▶ A representative of the Council for the Protection of Rural England.
▶ A member of the environmental pressure group, Greenpeace.
▶ A member of the Banbury and District Chamber of Commerce, representing local shopkeepers and tradespeople.

2 Read carefully the *press release from British Coal* (Figure B). Make sure that you understand it.

3 If you are not the person representing British Coal, read the *Submission to the Public Enquiry* which concerns your role (Figure C, facing page). Once you have all read the information turn to the next page.

British Coal PRESS RELEASE

New mines are vital to Britain's energy needs

The Oxfordshire coalfield offers a great opportunity for Britain to meet her coal needs for several decades into the future – at least 500 million tonnes of coal. The Oxfordshire coal is needed to increase national coal output and help provide replacement capacity for the output which will be lost by the exhaustion of existing reserves.

Plans to open new mines, particularly outside traditional mining areas, are bound to provoke anxiety about the effects on people who live there and their way of life. Our plans balance the best mining prospects with the least possible impact on the surrounding countryside and on those who live there.

However, the consequences for everybody's living standards will be much more severe if the limited time available is not used to ensure access to adequate supplies of coal – both as a fuel and a raw material – in the future.

When the demand for oil and gas begin to exceed supply the need for coal will increase. **IT IS ESSENTIAL THAT WE SAFEGUARD OUR COAL SUPPLIES NOW BY DEVELOPING THE OXFORDSHIRE COALFIELD.**

Figure B Press release from British Coal

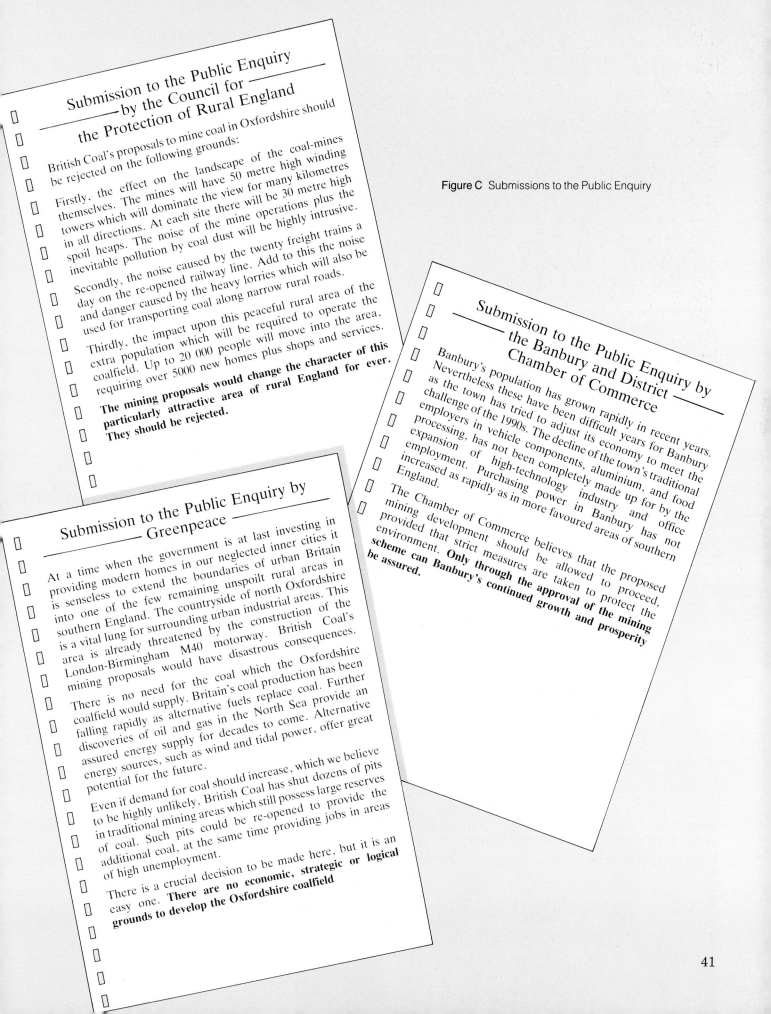

Figure C Submissions to the Public Enquiry

Submission to the Public Enquiry by the Council for the Protection of Rural England

British Coal's proposals to mine coal in Oxfordshire should be rejected on the following grounds:

Firstly, the effect on the landscape of the coal-mines themselves. The mines will have 50 metre high winding towers which will dominate the view for many kilometres in all directions. At each site there will be 30 metre high spoil heaps. The noise of the mine operations plus the inevitable pollution by coal dust will be highly intrusive.

Secondly, the noise caused by the twenty freight trains a day on the re-opened railway line. Add to this the noise and danger caused by the heavy lorries which will also be used for transporting coal along narrow rural roads.

Thirdly, the impact upon this peaceful rural area of the extra population which will be required to operate the coalfield. Up to 20 000 people will move into the area, requiring over 5000 new homes plus shops and services.

The mining proposals would change the character of this particularly attractive area of rural England for ever. They should be rejected.

Submission to the Public Enquiry by the Banbury and District Chamber of Commerce

Banbury's population has grown rapidly in recent years. Nevertheless these have been difficult years for Banbury as the town has tried to adjust its economy to meet the challenge of the 1990s. The decline of the town's traditional employers in vehicle components, aluminium, and food processing, has not been completely made up for by the expansion of high-technology industry and office employment. Purchasing power in Banbury has not increased as rapidly as in more favoured areas of southern England.

The Chamber of Commerce believes that the proposed mining development should be allowed to proceed, provided that strict measures are taken to protect the environment. **Only through the approval of the mining scheme can Banbury's continued growth and prosperity be assured.**

Submission to the Public Enquiry by Greenpeace

At a time when the government is at last investing in providing modern homes in our neglected inner cities it is senseless to extend the boundaries of urban Britain into one of the few remaining unspoilt rural areas in southern England. The countryside of north Oxfordshire is a vital lung for surrounding urban industrial areas. This area is already threatened by the construction of the London-Birmingham M40 motorway. British Coal's mining proposals would have disastrous consequences.

There is no need for the coal which the Oxfordshire coalfield would supply. Britain's coal production has been falling rapidly as alternative fuels replace coal. Further discoveries of oil and gas in the North Sea provide an assured energy supply for decades to come. Alternative energy sources, such as wind and tidal power, offer great potential for the future.

Even if demand for coal should increase, which we believe to be highly unlikely, British Coal has shut dozens of pits in traditional mining areas which still possess large reserves of coal. Such pits could be re-opened to provide the additional coal, at the same time providing jobs in areas of high unemployment.

There is a crucial decision to be made here, but it is an easy one. **There are no economic, strategic or logical grounds to develop the Oxfordshire coalfield**

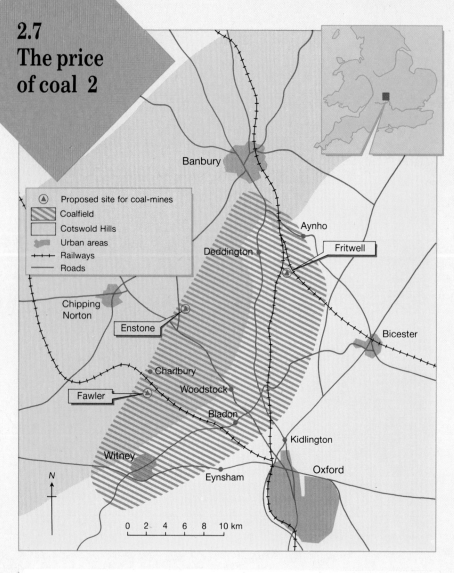

Figure A (*map*) British Coal's proposed mining developments in north Oxfordshire

Map labels: Banbury, Aynho, Fritwell, Deddington, Chipping Norton, Enstone, Bicester, Charlbury, Woodstock, Fawler, Bladon, Kidlington, Witney, Oxford, Eynsham

Legend:
- Proposed site for coal-mines
- Coalfield
- Cotswold Hills
- Urban areas
- Railways
- Roads

0 2 4 6 8 10 km

Figure B A modern coal-mine need not be unattractive

Discussion and Decision

Look at the map and photograph on this page, and read the summary of British Coal's proposals (facing page).

Now you are ready to discuss the proposals. Each member of the group, in alphabetical order, should present their submission to the group. There should be time for questions after each submission. After all four submissions are complete the group should hold a final discussion.

1 Now change roles. Each group member should now take on the role of Chairperson of the Public Enquiry. The Chairperson has to decide what course of action to recommend to the government. There are three choices.

The choices available

1 **Accept** British Coal's proposals and agree to the development proceeding according to their plan.
2 **Reject** British Coal's proposals completely and recommend that no development should be allowed at all.
3 **Amend** British Coal's proposals in any way you see fit in order to allow a modified development to proceed.

2 a) Write down a summary of the arguments for and against the proposed mining developments.
    b) Write down your decision and your reasons for it.

3 The decisions of each member of the class should be recorded by your teacher. What was the majority decision?

A summary of the proposal from British Coal to develop the Oxfordshire coalfield

The Oxfordshire coalfield comprises at least 500 million tonnes of general purpose and highly volatile steam coal. British Coal proposes to build three mines initially, at the sites shown on Figure A. The mines will be deep shaft mines requiring 50 metre high concrete winding towers at the pit-head, similar to those shown in Figure B. Modern coal-mines are more attractive buildings than older collieries. It will take twelve years to complete the three mines. An average of 50 hectares of land will be required for each mine.

It is proposed to mine two million tonnes of coal annually at each of the three mine sites. The coal will be washed at the pit-head and then transported by rail and road to inland markets, mainly power stations. It is estimated that there would be an average of one million tonnes a year of spoil from each of the three mine sites. British Coal propose that this should be tipped on sites near the mines after removal of topsoil and subsoil. The tip sites would be progressively restored to agricultural use with slopes generally no steeper than 1 in 8. The first part of the tips would be restored as quickly as possible to screen the mine sites both visually and acoustically from villages. Over a period of fifty years a total area of 250 hectares would be required at each mine for tipping.

British Coal does not believe that the nation can abandon the very valuable reserves of coal which Oxfordshire contains. If the coalfield is not developed the creation of new capacity will be greatly delayed because there are no alternative reserves of coal for which plans have reached a comparable stage of development.

Mine site	Description of site
Enstone	Disused airfield, mainly wasteland at present; over 5 km from nearest railway
Fritwell	Farmland site close to railways
Fawler	Attractive site in scenic valley of River Evenlode; close to railway

Figure C Summary of proposals

Oil is a source of energy and a raw material for many industries. What exactly is it, and how is it formed?

Oil is a mixture of hundreds of chemicals called hydrocarbons (because they contain hydrogen and carbon in varying amounts). The hydrocarbons are the chemical remains of billions of tiny sea creatures which died over 200 million years ago. When they died they sank to the sea-bed. Their tiny bodies were buried in mud brought down to the sea by rivers. Over millions of years the mud piled up in layers many hundreds of metres thick. This exerted a great pressure upon the lower layers. The pressure created heat. Time, pressure and heat created rock from the lower layers of mud, and turned the remains of the sea creatures into hydrocarbons. The lightest hydrocarbons are gases, the heavier ones liquid (crude oil) and the heaviest are solid (tar). Because of the enormous pressures the hydrocarbons seep slowly through the rocks. Sometimes they rise right to the surface and escape. More often they rise until they are trapped by impermeable rock. Figure A shows different types of oil trap. Large oil traps are called oilfields. The search for oilfields is a complex and expensive business.

Figure A Different types of oil trap

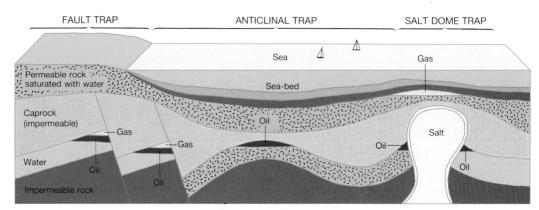

Figure B (*below*) World oil production and consumption

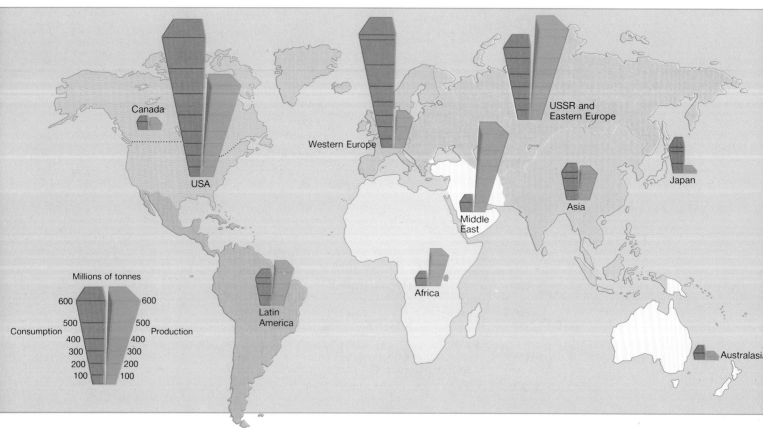

Oil production

The only sure way to find oil is to drill for it. Only one well in ten actually finds enough oil to produce. The search for oil has led the oil companies into some of the least welcoming areas of the earth: the deserts of Africa and the Middle East, the rain forest of South America, the Arctic wastes of Alaska, and the stormy depths of the North Sea. New methods have had to be developed to cope with each of these hostile environments.

Middle East oilfields produce cheap oil. They have low production costs, between $1 and $2 per barrel, because the oilfields are very large. Oil from Alaska costs as much as $10 per barrel to produce. Middle East oil has more of the lighter hydrocarbons. This 'light' oil fetches higher prices because it is easier to handle and refine.

Figure D Oil tanker and Royal Navy escort in the Persian Gulf, 1987

Asia and Latin America and the industrial nations of Europe, North America and Japan. So vital is this shipment of oil that the developed countries are prepared to send their navies to protect the tankers in times of danger. In 1987 navies from seven developed countries escorted their tankers through the Persian Gulf and the Straits of Hormuz, an area where tankers were regularly attacked during the Gulf War between Iran and Iraq (Figure D).

Figure C The top ten oil producing nations in 1980 and 1986

Country	Oil production (million tonnes)	
	1980	1986
USSR	605	619
USA	430	516
Saudi Arabia	480	271
Mexico	96	138
UK	81	127
China	105	122
Iran	73	89
Venezuela	108	88
United Arab Emirates	86	72
Libya	90	49

World distribution of oil

Oil has been discovered in many countries throughout the world (Figure B). Oil is in greatest demand in the countries of the developed world. They do not have enough oil to meet their demands and have to depend upon importing oil from developing countries.

Oil tankers sail constantly between the oilfields of the Middle East, Africa,

QUESTIONS

1 a) What is oil?
   b) List as many things as you can which are made from oil in the room you are currently in.

2 How is oil formed?

3 What is an oil trap?

4 Study Figure B.
   a) Name three areas which consume much more oil than they produce.
   b) Name three areas which produce more oil than they consume.
   c) How much oil do the following areas consume:
      (i) Western Europe (ii) the USA
      (iii) the USSR and Eastern Europe?
   d) How much oil do the following areas produce:
      (i) Western Europe (ii) the USA (iii) the Middle East?

5 Study Figure C showing the world's major oil producers.
   a) Draw a bar graph to illustrate the statistics for 1986.
   b) What changes have occurred in the oil production of these top ten countries between 1980 and 1986?
   c) What might have caused these changes?

6 a) Describe the scene in Figure D.
   b) Explain why this happened.

7 In 1987 it was estimated that the world's oil reserves would last for only another 33 years at present rates of consumption.
   a) Why is it likely that the world will actually still be using oil beyond the year 2020?
   b) What alternative sources of energy could be used instead of oil?

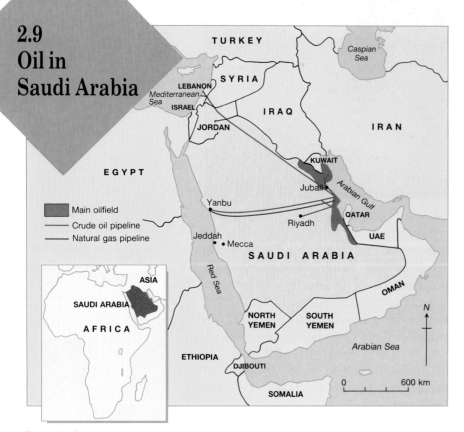

Figure A Saudi Arabia

Figure B (*above*) Tankers loading oil at the Ras Tanura terminal

Figure C (*right*) Saudi Arabia's oil production, 1950–85

The world's largest oilfields have been discovered in the Middle East. Saudi Arabia has the largest reserves, over 30 billion tonnes. The search for oil in Saudi Arabia was begun in 1933 by a consortium of US companies called Aramco. Saudi Arabia was one of the poorest countries in the world and the Saudi government was happy to receive a small payment from Aramco for the rights to market any oil found. This must have been the sale of the century!

Aramco made the first big discovery in 1938. Large-scale production began ten years later. In 1950 the Saudi government negotiated a 50 per cent share of Aramco's profits. In 1973 the government bought 25 per cent of Aramco's shares, increased to 60 per cent in 1974. After long and difficult negotiations, the Saudis took over Aramco completely in 1980, paying over $1 billion to the US companies in compensation.

There are 14 major oilfields in Saudi Arabia, all in the east of the country. Some of them lie offshore in the Arabian (or Persian) Gulf. Saudi Arabia's oil production reached a peak of 480 million tonnes a year in 1980 (Figure C). A fall in demand for oil since 1980 has caused a decline in production. Despite this, oil has made Saudi Arabia one of the richest countries in the world.

Oil revenues have been used in a variety of ways:

● To develop a reliable supply of freshwater. A network of desalination plants turn seawater into freshwater.

● To provide a very high standard of social services including free education, medicine and medical care.

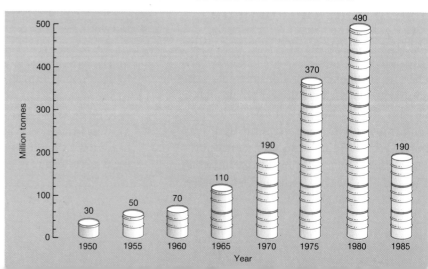

- To provide a modern *infrastructure* including mains water, electricity and sewerage, telephones, roads, airports and sea ports.
- To develop farming in order to reduce food imports.
- To develop manufacturing industry.
- To provide economic aid to poorer nations. Between 1980 and 1985 Saudi Arabia gave $24 billion to over 70 countries.

Saudi Arabia's main aim is to create a modern economic society providing an assured standard of living which can be maintained when the oil runs out.

Most of Saudi Arabia's oil is exported as crude petroleum. In recent years the Saudi government has encouraged the development of an oil refining and petro-chemical industry to provide employment and increase export earnings. There are eleven petro-chemical plants and two oil refineries at the new town of Jubail. Other industries have been encouraged also, including steel, cement, aluminium, copper and light industries. Oil and gas pipelines have been laid across the country to the new city of Yanbu on the Red Sea coast where many factories have been built.

Agriculture in Saudi Arabia

Irrigation has allowed the desert to bloom. In 1983 Saudi Arabia grew 0.5 million tonnes of wheat. By 1986 over 2 million tonnes of wheat was harvested. The Saudi government had introduced subsidies to Saudi wheat farmers of up to ten times the price of imported wheat.

Consumption of wheat in Saudi Arabia amounts to one million tonnes per year. Saudi farmers are now over-producing wheat and the government is tryng to cut back on wheat and boost barley production. Barley is a vital feedstuff for the rapidly growing livestock farms. Low interest loans have been provided for land and machinery as well as subsidies for fertilizer, water, fuel and electricity. Saudi Arabia is now self-sufficient in milk, eggs and chicken meat. In fact, cow's milk is now exported to neighbouring countries.

Figure D The King Faisal Centre, Riyadh – an example of the impressive modern architecture in Saudi Arabia

Figure E (*below*) Saudi Arabia's GDP by sector (percentage shares), 1982 and 1985

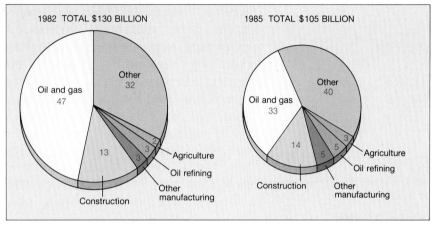

QUESTIONS

1 a) Where is Saudi Arabia?
 b) Why is Saudi Arabia important in the world oil industry?

2 Study Figure C.
 a) What was Saudi Arabia's oil production in
  (i) 1950 (ii) 1960 (iii) 1970 (iv) 1980 (v) 1985?
 b) How do you explain the pattern shown by the graph?

3 How has Saudi Arabia used its revenues from oil?

4 Study the table below:

Production of petroleum products

Country	Petroleum products (million tonnes)	
	1970	**1983**
Saudi Arabia	26	41
Kuwait	17	22
United Arab Emirates	0	5
UK	91	70
West Germany	94	77
France	89	68

 a) What trends are revealed in the table?
 b) How do you explain these trends?

5 Study the two pie graphs (Figure E).
 a) Describe the changes in Saudi Arabia's GDP by sector between 1982 and 1985.
 b) Explain these changes.
 c) What changes would you expect in Saudi Arabia's GDP in the future?

When Botswana became independent from Britain in 1966 it faced an uncertain future. Britain had done little to develop the country because it had few natural resources; even water and fertile soil were in short supply. The newly independent state was one of the poorest in Africa.

In 1966 agriculture was the main sector of the economy. Most of the population were subsistence farmers. A small number of commercial cattle ranchers were responsible for most of the country's export earnings through the sale of beef and live cattle, mainly to South Africa.

The big breakthrough for Botswana was the discovery of minerals in the late 1960s: copper, nickel, coal, and, most important of all, diamonds. The production of minerals has brought big changes to Botswana's economy.

Figure B Orapa township – a modern town isolated in the dry savanna of Botswana

fence and only mining employees are allowed inside. The mining company even runs its own farms.

Orapa township is strangely out of place in the Botswana scrubland. It is a self-contained unit inhabited mainly by foreigners and has little effect upon the surrounding countryside. A road has been built linking Orapa with the railway at Francistown 250 km to the east. The diamonds are sorted at Gaborone, but only a few are cut and finished there. Most are flown out to London for finishing and valuation.

Diamond production was 13 million carats in 1986, 15 per cent of the total world production. Diamond exports made up 76 per cent of Botswana's export earnings. Only half the profits from diamond sales go to the Botswanan government, the rest is taken by De Beers and mainly spent outside Botswana.

Figure A Botswana

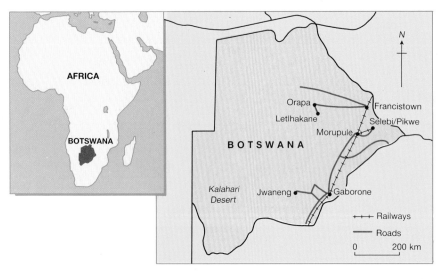

Diamonds

Diamonds were first discovered at Letlhakane in 1967 and later at Orapa and Jwaneng (Figure A). Botswana had no money to develop the diamond mining and so had to depend upon a foreign multi-national company, De Beers. Mining townships have been built at the three sites. The largest is at Orapa where a town of over 3000 people includes a school, a hospital, shops and a diesel power station. A reservoir has been constructed to supply water. The township is surrounded by a security

Copper and nickel

Large deposits of copper and nickel were discovered at Selebi/Pikwe. The Botswanan government took the leading role in developing mining. Four thousand miners work here. Unlike Orapa, there has been rapid migration into the township and its population has grown from 5000 in 1971 to over 30 000 by 1986. A rail link has been established as well as new roads, water supply and a coal-fired power station. Unfortunately the world price of copper has fallen steadily since the 1970s and Botswana has made little money out of its copper. The great cost of developing the mine has left Botswana deeply in debt.

Coal

Coal-mining started at Morupule in 1973. This small open-cast mine produces 250 000 tonnes of coal per year. A much larger mine opened at Kgaswe in 1982 with a potential annual production of 5 million tonnes. However, coal prices were too low to earn a profit from the mine and it only produces about 200 000 tonnes a year to meet local demand.

There have been many advantages to Botswana from mineral development (Figure D). With a GDP per person of $1045, Botswana is one of Africa's wealthier nations. The government has tried to spend money on improving agriculture, but has been forced to spend much of its income on repaying the loans needed to establish the mines. Little of the new wealth has reached the average person in Botswana. It is estimated that 90 per cent of Botswana's 1.1 million people work outside the modern economy. Most are subsistence cattle herders. The adult literacy rate is only 25 per cent and the infant mortality rate is high at 72 deaths per thousand births.

Botswana's mining and manufacturing are largely controlled by South Africa, which also supplies most of Botswana's imports. The Botswanan government faces a big challenge in sharing the benefits of mining among more of the people.

Figure D The advantages and disadvantages of mining for Botswana

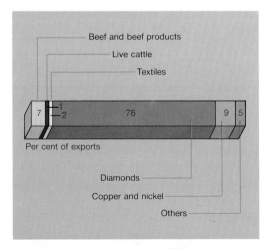

Figure C Botswana's exports, 1986

QUESTIONS

1 Find a map of Southern Africa in your atlas.
  a) Make your own copy of Figure A.
  b) Using your atlas to help you, (i) describe the location of Botswana (ii) name the countries bordering Botswana.
  c) What is the average January temperature over much of Botswana?
  d) What is the average rainfall in Botswana?
  e) Find the map showing population distribution in Africa in your atlas. Describe the distribution of population in Botswana and try to explain it.

2 Figure C shows Botswana's exports in 1986.
  a) Draw a similar divided bar graph to show Botswana's exports in 1966 using the following figures:

Botswana's exports in 1966

Commodity	Percentage of total export earnings
Beef and beef products	95
Live cattle	3
Textiles	2

  b) How did Botswana's export trade change between 1966 and 1986?
  c) Why is it important for Botswana to sell a variety of goods to other countries?

3 a) Why is Orapa township 'strangely out of place in Botswana'?
  b) Why do you think that Botswana's diamond mines are run jointly with the foreign multi-national company De Beers?
  c) Diamond mining affects few people in Botswana and brings the ordinary people few benefits. Why is this?

4 In your own words explain the effects of mineral development on Botswana.

Unit 2 ASSESSMENT

1 What is an ore? (1 mark)

2 How do the following methods of mining differ:
(a) open-cast (b) drift (c) shaft? (3 marks)

3 a) What is kaolin? (1 mark)
b) How is kaolin formed? (3 marks)
c) Give four uses of kaolin. (2 marks)
d) Where is kaolin mined in the UK? (1 mark)

4 Quarries such as the one shown in the photograph
(Figure A) may cause environmental problems.
a) State two environmental problems caused by this
quarry. (2 marks)
b) Name two groups of people who would probably
oppose the development of such a quarry. (2 marks)
c) Give two arguments in favour of this kind of
quarrying. (4 marks)

5 a) Name one coalfield in a developed country which has
suffered a severe decline in output in recent years.
(1 mark)
b) State three factors which have led to the decline in
output. (6 marks)
c) What effects has the decline in output had upon your
named region? (5 marks)
d) What measures might be taken to help overcome such
effects? (4 marks)

6 a) Name one developing country whose economy is
based upon the export of crude oil. (1 mark)
b) Describe what the money earned from oil exports has
been spent on. (5 marks)

Figure A A limestone quarry in the Mendip Hills,
South-West England

c) Study Figure B which shows the world price of crude oil, in dollars per barrel, in the period between December 1985 and December 1987.

  (i) During which period was the price of crude oil reasonably stable? (1 mark)

  (ii) What was the price of crude oil in December 1985? (1 mark)

  (iii) By how much did the price of crude oil fall between 1 December 1985 and early July 1986? (1 mark)

  (iv) What would be the effects of such a fall in the price of oil for the developing country you named in answer to 6a)? (6 marks)

TOTAL: 50 marks

Figure B The world price of crude oil

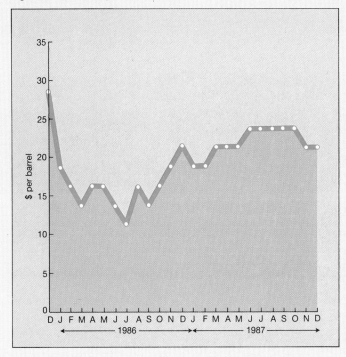

Details for pupil profile sheet Unit 2

Knowledge and understanding

1 Minerals

2 Ores

3 Lodes

4 Methods of mining: open-cast, drift, shaft

5 Kaolin

6 Formation of coal

7 Exposed, concealed coalfield

8 Formation of oil

9 Oil traps

10 Infrastructure

Skills

1 Draw labelled diagrams

2 Draw a bar graph

3 Group work

4 Writing a summary

5 Role play

6 Written description from a photograph

7 Draw a divided bar

8 Read a line graph

9 Decision making

10 Reading a pie graph

Values

1 Awareness of the environmental effects of mining

2 Awareness of the role of multi-national companies in a developing country

3 Awareness of developing world debt

Unit 3: Energy

Study Figure A, **answer question 1** and then continue to read the text.

Figure A Energy consumption contrasts

Country	Percentage of world's population	Percentage of world's energy consumption
USA	5	30
India	16	2

Figure B (*below*) In these two maps the countries are scaled according to their production and consumption of oil

The world's energy resources are not evenly distributed. Most of the world's oil, coal and gas are concentrated in the developed countries. The developed countries use much more energy than the developing countries (Figure A). The economic growth of most developed countries has been based upon their own resources of oil and coal and, as these reserves run low, they import increasing amounts from developing countries.

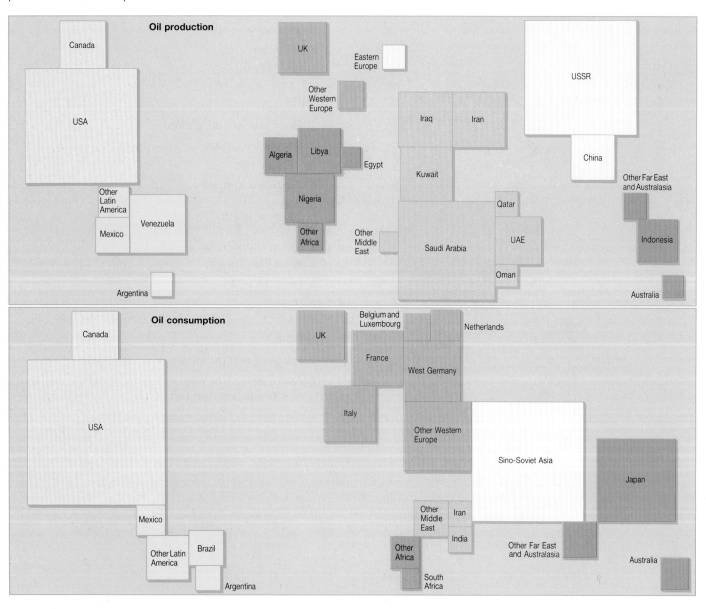

The average American consumes over three hundred times as much energy as the average person in Burkina Faso!

Figure C The consumption of energy per person in selected countries

Country	Consumption of energy per person (Kg of coal equivalent)	
	1970	1986
Burkina Faso	20	28
Brazil	440	720
France	3840	3840
India	140	260
Saudi Arabia	470	3670
Singapore	2010	5450
South Korea	670	1650
UK	4870	4700
USA	10820	9300

Until the 'Oil Crisis' of 1973 (see 5.4) energy consumption was increasing rapidly in the developed countries. Since 1973 the rate of increase has slowed and in some countries less energy is now consumed. This is partly due to the economic recession, which has reduced the demand for energy by manufacturing industry, and partly due to better conservation of energy. Energy conservation measures include:

● Improved design of motor vehicles. This has reduced petrol consumption. Ford's 'lean burn' engine offers a 10 per cent cut in petrol.

● The increasing use of more economical diesel engines in cars.

● Increased insulation of houses. This has reduced heat loss and cut energy use.

● Solar panels on a house roof can cut water heating bills.

● Electrical appliances such as televisions and refrigerators have been made more fuel-efficient, so consuming less electricity.

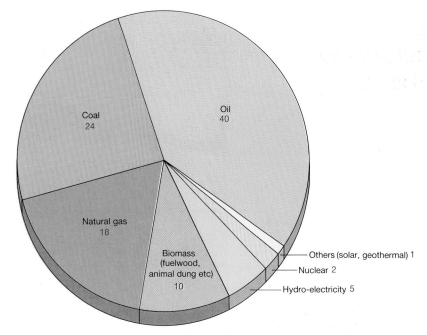

Figure D The sources of world energy (per cent), 1987

QUESTIONS

1 a) What percentage of the world's population lives in
   (i) the USA (ii) India?
 b) What percentage of the world's energy is consumed in
   (i) the USA (ii) India?
 c) What does this tell you about the levels of development of the two countries?

2 Study Figure D.
 a) What percentage of the world's energy consumption consists of (i) oil (ii) coal (iii) natural gas?
 b) Which of the energy sources listed in the pie graph are
   (i) renewable (ii) non-renewable?
 c) What percentage of the world's energy consumption consists of renewable energy sources?

3 Study Figure C.
 a) Name the three countries with the highest consumption of energy per person in 1986.
 b) Which two countries showed a reduction of consumption of energy per person between 1970 and 1986?
 c) What has caused this reduction in energy consumption?
 d) Which three countries showed the highest percentage increase in consumption of energy per person between 1970 and 1986?
 e) What do you think may have caused this increase in energy consumption?

4 Study Figure B.
 a) What do these unusual world maps show?
 b) Name the five major oil producing nations.
 c) Name the five major oil consuming nations.
 d) Which major oil producing nations consume very little oil themselves?
 e) Which major oil consuming country produces very little oil itself?

Figure A

Figure B Energy consumption by source in the UK, 1973–86

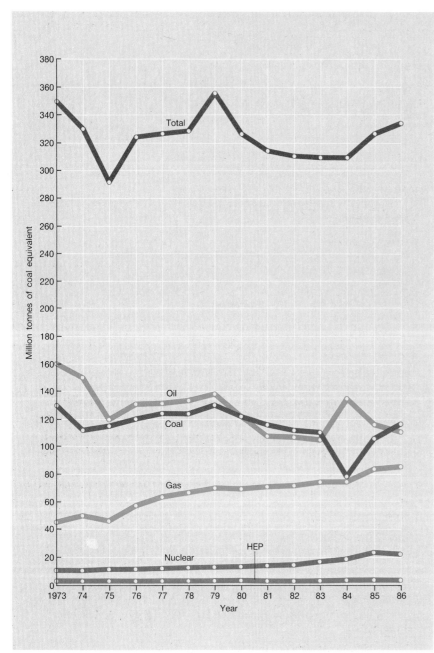

Figure A shows a vanished age, the age of coal. Coal was the dominant form of energy used in the UK for over a century. Coal was plentiful and cheap. It had a variety of uses including:

- *fuel* for steam engines
- *fuel* for homes, factories and offices
- the production of *gas*
- the production of *chemicals* such as tar, sulphuric acid and ammonia

British homes were designed to cope with coal. Near the back door would be the coal bunker. There were open hearths on which coal and wood fires were burnt.

Open coal fires look very attractive, but they have many problems. Coal is dirty, heavy and difficult to use. Rooms can fill with smoke when a door is

Figure C Sources of energy consumed in the UK, 1986 (by percentage of total in coal equivalent)

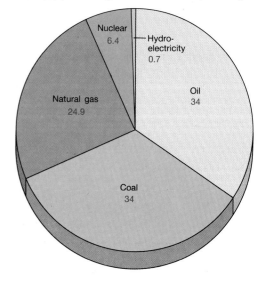

opened! When the fire is finished, soot and ash are left. The hearth has to be cleared and the waste placed in a heavy steel dustbin outside. Open fires can be dangerous; many homes have been destroyed by blazes started by coal fires which had not been closely watched.

Alternative forms of energy have become widely available in the UK since the 1960s. Oil, gas and electricity provide most of the country's energy. It is not all bad news for coal, however, because it is still the most important fuel used to generate electricity. New, cleaner methods of using coal to heat houses have been developed.

Oil, gas and electricity are much cleaner and easier to use than coal. The price of the different forms of energy is also an important factor:

● During the 1960s oil and gas became cheaper while the price of coal rose. Demand for coal fell dramatically.

● In 1973/74 the Oil Crisis (see 5.4) made oil much more expensive. Gas and coal were cheaper. Gas took a larger share of the energy market as the North Sea gasfields were developed. There was even a revival in the use of coal. This was reinforced by the great oil price increases of 1979/80.

● In 1986 oil became much cheaper. Demand for coal fell again.

The changing demands for energy have had great effects on the geography of the UK since 1960. Half a million coal mining jobs have been lost as hundreds of coal-mines have closed. Oil and gas rigs have been sited in the seas around the country. Oil and gas terminals have sprung up on the coast. Thousands of kilometres of pipelines carry gas and oil around the country. Giant new nuclear power stations have been built.

Price and ease of use have been the major factors affecting the changing energy demand in the UK in the last forty years. In the future the exhaustion of energy sources will become important. The world's oil supplies may

not last more than another forty years. Much of the world's oil and gas is located in areas which have suffered conflict, such as the Middle East. Supplies may be cut off from the UK for political reasons, as they were, briefly, during 1956 and 1973. Home energy sources, of which coal is the largest, will then become more important for the UK again.

Past experience shows that there are no certainties in demand for energy within the UK. The future may hold many changes.

Figure D The natural gas terminal at Bacton, Norfolk

QUESTIONS

1 Study Figure B.
   a) What was the total energy consumption in the UK in
      (i) 1973 (ii) 1981 (iii) 1986?
   b) Which energy source was most important in
      (i) 1973 (ii) 1981 (iii) 1986?
   c) Which energy source increased most between 1973 and 1986?
   d) Which energy source decreased most between 1973 and 1986?

2 a) Using the information provided by Figure B, draw a pie graph similar to Figure C to show the sources of energy consumed in the UK in 1973.
   b) How has the pattern of energy consumption in the UK changed between 1973 and 1986?

3 What were the problems with coal as a domestic fuel?

4 What are the advantages of oil, gas and electricity over coal?

5 Give four effects which the changing demands for energy have had upon the UK.

6 How may the following factors affect the future energy demands in the UK: (a) the exhaustion of energy sources, and (b) political factors?

Figure A

A lightning flash. One of nature's most dramatic events. The lightning is a giant electrical spark, the glowing path traced by billions of tiny particles called electrons.

The lightning carries electricity for only an instant. If people wish to use electricity they need something which will give a continuous stream of it, not a single spark. A continuous stream of electricity is called an electric current.

How is an electric current made? The most important way is by using a machine called an alternator. This turns motion into electricity. In order to make large amounts of electricity the alternator must be very large and it must be driven at very high speed by another machine called a turbine. The turbine itself must be spun at very high speed, by steam, running water or the wind.

Eighty-five per cent of the electricity used in Britain is generated by power stations using a fossil fuel (coal, oil or gas). Coal is the most important. The coal is burnt in a boiler which turns water to steam. The steam is forced under high pressure into the turbine (Figure B).

Figure B How electricity is made in a coal-fired power station

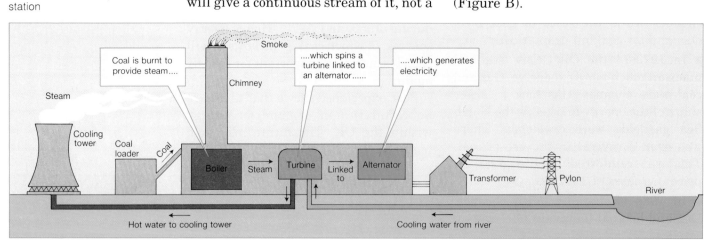

The location of fossil-fuel power stations

Coal-fired generators. Since coal is bulky and expensive to transport, most coal-fired power stations are on or near coalfields. The Trent Valley is the most important location. Eleven power stations have been built there, using coal from the nearby Yorkshire, Nottinghamshire and Derbyshire coalfields. The river provides cooling water and its valley floor provides suitable flat sites. Another important location is the Lower Thames where there are six coal-fired stations. Coal is not available locally, but it can be shipped easily down the east coast. The main locating

Figure C   The 2000 MW coal-fired power station at Cottam in the Trent Valley

factors are the great demand for electricity from London and the large supplies of cooling water from the Thames.

Oil-fired generators. These are located near oil refineries and away from coalfields. No new oil-fired power stations have been started since the early 1970s when oil prices rose dramatically.

Gas-fired generators. Most are small gas turbine units, using converted jet engines. Many are for emergency use only. They are located mainly in areas remote from other power stations, like the Isle of Wight and East Anglia.

The national grid

Electricity is transmitted throughout Britain by a network of cables called the national grid. The main cables are called the supergrid, and transmit electricity at 400 000 volts. Smaller cables carry electricity at lower voltages from this supergrid to the customer.

Unfortunately, electricity is gradually lost as it is transmitted. The further it has to travel, the greater the loss. Since the 1970s increasing amounts of electricity have been needed in the south of England, while the north requires less. This is because of the decline of heavy industry in the north, once the major customer for electricity. Demand in the south has increased because of the growth of high-tech industry, much of it requiring large amounts of electricity to power computers and other electronic devices.

In 1987 plans were announced to build two new coal-fired power stations, both next to existing stations. One is in the traditional coal-fired location of the Trent Valley. The second, however, is in the south of England, at Fawley in Hampshire. Fawley is the site of a large oil-fired power station. By building a coal-fired station at Fawley, as well as new nuclear stations, it is hoped to supply the increasing electricity demands of the south of England into the next century.

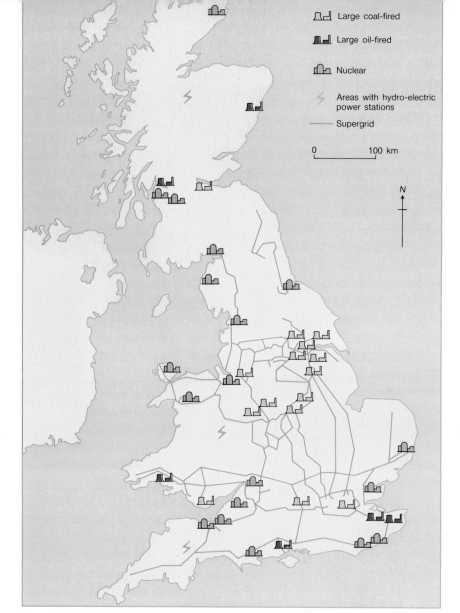

Figure D The supergrid and major power stations

QUESTIONS

1 Make a list of twenty things in your home which use electricity.

2 a) What is an electric current?
 b) How is an electric current made?

3 Using Figure B, construct a flow chart showing how electricity is generated at a coal-fired power station.

4 Explain why (i) the Trent Valley and (ii) the Lower Thames Valley are suitable locations for coal-fired power stations.

5 a) What is the supergrid?
 b) What geographical problem faces electricity supply in England?
 c) How is it planned to overcome this problem?

6 There is concern about the effect of coal-burning power stations on the atmosphere. This is called the 'Greenhouse Effect'.
 a) Find out what is meant by the 'Greenhouse Effect'.
 b) What can be done to reduce the problem?

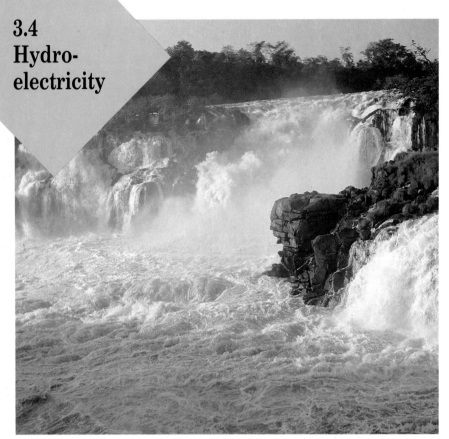

Four thousand cubic metres of water per second plunges over this waterfall. That's a cubic kilometre of water every four minutes! In terms of volume of water it is the greatest waterfall in the world. This is the Guaira Falls on the River Parana in Brazil.

The energy of falling water can be used to produce power. People have created hydro-electric turbines which are spun by falling water. The spinning turbines are linked to alternators which generate electricity. Hydro-electric power (HEP) has many advantages, and some disadvantages (Figure B).

The Guaira Falls shown in Figure A have disappeared. How? Drowned by the reservoir formed behind the Itaipu Dam, part of the world's largest hydro-electric scheme.

Figure A (*photograph, left*)

Figure B How an HEP station generates electricity, and the advantages and disadvantages of hydro-electricity

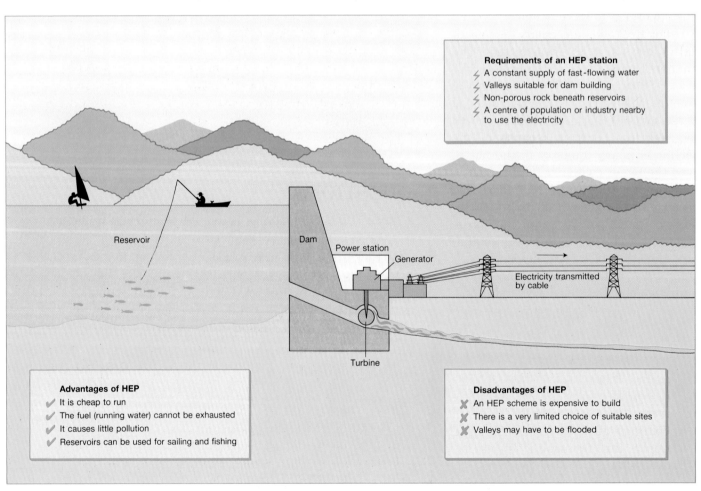

Requirements of an HEP station
- A constant supply of fast-flowing water
- Valleys suitable for dam building
- Non-porous rock beneath reservoirs
- A centre of population or industry nearby to use the electricity

Reservoir

Dam

Power station

Generator

Electricity transmitted by cable

Turbine

Advantages of HEP
- It is cheap to run
- The fuel (running water) cannot be exhausted
- It causes little pollution
- Reservoirs can be used for sailing and fishing

Disadvantages of HEP
- An HEP scheme is expensive to build
- There is a very limited choice of suitable sites
- Valleys may have to be flooded

The Itaipu Dam is 8.5 km wide and 190 m high. It was completed in 1982. It took seven years to build and is the world's largest concrete structure, higher than London's tallest building and twice the volume of the Great Pyramid in Egypt! Behind the dam the river waters rose and flooded an area covering 1400 square kilometres. The 200 km long reservoir submerged the Guaira Falls and the homes of 20 000 people who were forced to move.

The dam was built at a site where the River Parana flows in a narrow section, forming the border between Brazil and Paraguay. The Itaipu Dam has eighteen turbines. The fast-flowing waters of the Parana are forced to pass through the sluices of the dam and spin the giant turbines. The alternators linked to the turbines each generate 700 megawatts of electricity (1 MW is one million watts). The power station has a total capacity of 12 600 MW (Britain's largest HEP station has a capacity of only 1 800 MW). Although half this power belongs to Paraguay the Paraguayans use only about 500 MW and so they sell the rest to Brazil.

The Itaipu project cost $12 billion. New towns have been built on both sides of the river at Itaipu. They were

Figure D The Itaipu Dam viewed from the Brazilian side

built to house the construction workers and their families, plus the people displaced by the reservoir.

Despite the vast scale of the Itaipu project, it represents only five years growth in Brazil's electricity demand. By 1990 Brazil will have an installed capacity of 77 500 MW of hydro-electricity. Other large HEP schemes are already under construction for the 1990s.

Figure C The Itaipu HEP project

QUESTIONS

1 How does a hydro-electric power station produce electricity?

2 What are (a) the advantages (b) the disadvantages of hydro-electric power?

3 What has happened to the Guaira Falls?

4 a) Where is the Itaipu HEP project?
   b) Why was this a good site to build an HEP station?
   c) What is the electrical capacity of Itaipu?

5 You work as a reporter for a television company. You have been instructed to fly to Brazil in order to make a four-minute-long film presentation on the Itaipu Dam and its effects. Your film will be broadcast in a news programme.
   a) Describe the six scenes which your camera team will film.
   b) Write the commentary to your film. If you have access to a cassette recorder you should record your commentary. Make sure that your commentary is accurate, informative and interesting.

3.5 Nuclear power 1

Figure A

A nuclear bomb explodes and gives off enough energy to destroy a city. Since the 1940s the threat of nuclear weapons has haunted the world. But nuclear energy also holds a great hope for the future: a dream of cheap, clean, safe power.

The UK was at the forefront of nuclear power. The world's first commercial nuclear power station was opened in 1956 at Calder Hall in Cumbria. By 1987 there were 38 nuclear reactors in service, generating 19 per cent of the UK's electricity. Nuclear power stations use uranium as a fuel. Uranium is a *radioactive* element: it naturally releases energy in the form of radiation. Unfortunately, radiation is harmful to plants, animals and people. A large dose can kill immediately; smaller doses can lead to death through cancer.

A nuclear power station is similar to fossil-fuel power stations in that it turns water into steam to drive a turbine linked to an alternator. The heat needed to turn the water into steam is produced in a *nuclear reactor*. Fuel rods of uranium are lowered into the reactor core. The uranium atoms are split in a controlled chain-reaction called *nuclear fission*, which creates intense heat. The heat is transferred to the boilers to create steam.

Nuclear power stations use only small amounts of uranium as fuel, so they are not tied to their fuel source in the same way as fossil-fuel power stations. The most important requirement is a large amount of cooling water (up to 4000 million litres are used each day by a single nuclear power station). All British nuclear power stations are built on the coast, with the single exception of Trawsfynydd which has its own lake. The early nuclear power stations were built in fairly remote areas where less people were at risk in the event of an accident. A serious leak of radiation from a reactor at Windscale in Cumbria in 1957 showed some of the dangers.

There are two types of nuclear power station in the UK, *magnox* and *advanced gas-cooled reactors* (AGRs). The early magnox stations are nearing the end of their active life. The more modern AGRs use enriched uranium fuel. As a result of high costs and delay to the AGR programme, the Central Electricity Generating Board (CEGB) has turned to the US-designed *pressurized water reactor* (PWR) which they say will be cheaper and easier to build. The PWR uses water as a 'moderator' within the reactor. Magnox and AGR stations use graphite. A leak of the pressurized water could be disas-

Figure B How a nuclear power station generates electricity

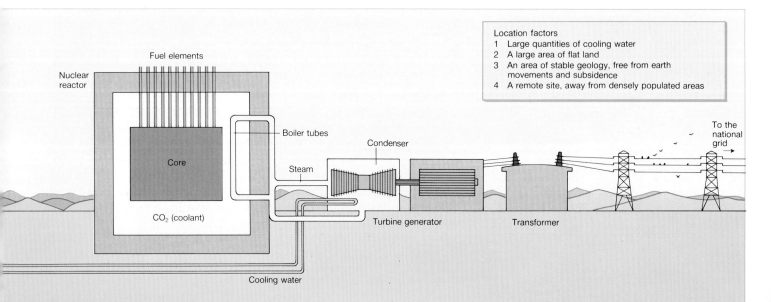

Nuclear reactor

Fuel elements

Core

CO_2 (coolant)

Boiler tubes

Steam

Cooling water

Condenser

Turbine generator

Transformer

To the national grid

Location factors
1 Large quantities of cooling water
2 A large area of flat land
3 An area of stable geology, free from earth movements and subsidence
4 A remote site, away from densely populated areas

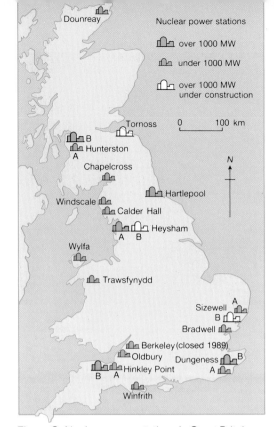

Figure C   Nuclear power stations in Great Britain

Figure D   (*above*) The AGR at Hartlepool

Figure E   An advertisement from the Nuclear Electricity Information Group

trous. After a fierce debate and a long Public Enquiry, permission was given for the CEGB to build its first PWR at Sizewell in Suffolk.

Nuclear waste

Dangerously radioactive uranium fuel rods are removed from the reactor core after seven years' use and stored in cooling ponds until their radiation levels have fallen. They are then taken by rail to a reprocessing plant at Sellafield (previously Windscale). Up to 2 tonnes of spent fuel elements are carried in massive steel flasks weighing 50 tonnes. The flasks are designed to survive rail accident and fire, but their transport through built-up areas is opposed by anti-nuclear groups.

At Sellafield the waste parts of the fuel rods are converted into liquid and stored. There is at present no way of making this high-level waste safe. Research is under way to find permanent disposal methods. The possibility of dumping material in deep shafts has met with strong local opposition wherever it has been proposed.

QUESTIONS

1 What is the fuel used in nuclear power stations?

2 What is a radioactive element?

3 With the aid of a simple flow diagram, describe how a nuclear power station produces electricity.

4 List the factors affecting the location of nuclear power stations.

5 a) What do the letters AGR and PWR stand for?
   b) Why has the CEGB decided to build a PWR?
   c) Where will the UK's first PWR be built?

6 a) What problems are posed by the disposal of radioactive nuclear waste?
   b) How far have they been overcome?

7 Study Figure E.
   a) What is the purpose of this advertisement?
   b) What impressions does the advertisement give of the opponents of nuclear power?
   c) Design a poster either supporting or opposing nuclear power. Make sure that your message gets over effectively.

Figure A The burnt-out reactor at Chernobyl

On 26 April 1986 a leak of hydrogen gas caused an explosion and fire in Reactor No.4 at Chernobyl nuclear power station in the USSR. Courageous firemen prevented the fire spreading to the other reactors, but at the cost of their own lives. The firemen were killed by *radiation* because the core of the reactor was exposed by the blast. A giant *radioactive* cloud drifted across Europe. At first the Russians did not reveal the disaster, but radioactivity was soon picked up in Sweden and the news was broadcast around the world.

Over the following few days the radioactive cloud drifted back and forth across Europe, casting a shadow of death across the continent. It has been estimated that in Europe as a whole up to 2000 people will die from cancers due to the radioactive fallout. In the USSR the final figure could be much higher. Only two people were killed in the fire, but by September thirty-five Russians, including the brave firemen, had died from radiation sickness.

The Chernobyl disaster caused 135 000 people to be evacuated from the surrounding area. Food and milk had to be destroyed. As far away as Britain, measures were taken to prevent the slaughter of sheep which had grazed contaminated grass in the mountains of Wales and the Lake District. The ban lasted for several years after the disaster and cost many farmers a lot of money. Poland claimed that it had lost over £6 million because 40 000 tourists had cancelled holidays for fear of the radiation. The way of life of the Sami (Lapps) in Scandinavia was devastated by the build up of radioactivity in their reindeer which grazed contaminated moss and lichen. Their survival depends upon their reindeer. None of the reindeer meat could be safely eaten in 1986.

Chernobyl cast a cloud over the future of nuclear power. Public opposition to nuclear power increased. The great dreams of a future based entirely on cheap, clean nuclear electricity have long since died.

Nuclear power in France

No country has adopted nuclear power with more enthusiasm than France. In 1973 only 8 per cent of France's electricity was generated by nuclear power. By 1988 the figure was over 65 per cent. France had depended heavily upon imported oil, the price of which increased enormously in 1973. A massive nuclear power programme was made a priority after 1973.

By 1981, thirty-three 900 MW and eleven 1300 MW nuclear power stations were in operation or under construction. The programme was cut back by 20 per cent when the new government of President Mitterand took office in 1981. The nuclear programme has been strongly opposed by ecologists on safety grounds. Their arguments were made stronger by the Chernobyl disaster.

Despite the cut-backs, nuclear power output in France is now second only to that of the USA. By 1992 there should be 61 nuclear power stations producing 75 per cent of France's electricity. Nuclear power is cheap. The nuclear power stations produce electricity at 23 centimes per kilowatt-hour (kWh) compared with 35 centimes for electricity from coal and 80 centimes for electricity from oil.

The threat of another Chernobyl-style disaster is dismissed as impossible

Figure C The nuclear power station at Chinon, France

by French electricity officials. Disposing of the nuclear waste is certainly a problem however. The highly radioactive waste products and fuel rods have to be reprocessed and then stored. Plans to dump the dangerous waste at sea or in deep mines have been rejected. At present the waste is stored, closely guarded, awaiting the discovery of a safe means of disposal. Some of the waste remains lethal for centuries!

Figure B Electricity production from nuclear power in selected West European countries

Country	Percentage of total electricity production		
	1980	1985	1995 (estimate)
UK	13	19	26
France	24	65	75
West Germany	11	31	33
Italy	1	4	13
Spain	5	22	30
Belgium	23	63	66
Netherlands	6	6	13
Sweden	22	42	47
Switzerland	28	40	36

QUESTIONS

1 a) Where is Chernobyl?
   b) What happened there in April 1986?

2 What were the effects of the Chernobyl disaster?

3 Why has France adopted a massive nuclear power programme?

4 Why is nuclear waste a problem?

5 a) Which country in Figure B had the highest percentage of its electricity generated by nuclear power stations in (i) 1980 and (ii) 1985?
   b) Which is the only country that planned to reduce the percentage contribution of nuclear power by 1995?
   c) What effect do you think the Chernobyl disaster might have on the actual contribution of nuclear power by 1995?

6 a) Do you think that nuclear power is safe?
   b) Should more nuclear power stations be built?
   c) Carry out a survey among the pupils at your school to find out their views on nuclear power. What questions could you ask? How many pupils do you need to ask?

Figure A shows a remarkable power station. It generates electricity by harnessing the energy in the tides. The tidal power station is on the River Rance in France.

Opened in 1966, the Rance tidal power station is a hollow dam over 700 m wide across the river estuary. Twenty-four turbines are housed in the dam. They are spun by the fast-flowing tidal current and generate 240 MW of electricity. The tidal range in the Rance Estuary is the third highest in the world, producing a head of 12 m of water.

The electricity generated by the Rance power station is not as cheap as you might think. Varying tide levels mean that much water has to be pumped above the barrage. There are no plans to repeat this costly scheme in France.

For many years the Rance was the only tidal power station in the world. In 1984 a second, much smaller, example opened at Annapolis Royal on the Bay of Fundy, Canada, the site of the world's

Figure A The Rance tidal power station in France

Figure B The Severn Barrage proposals

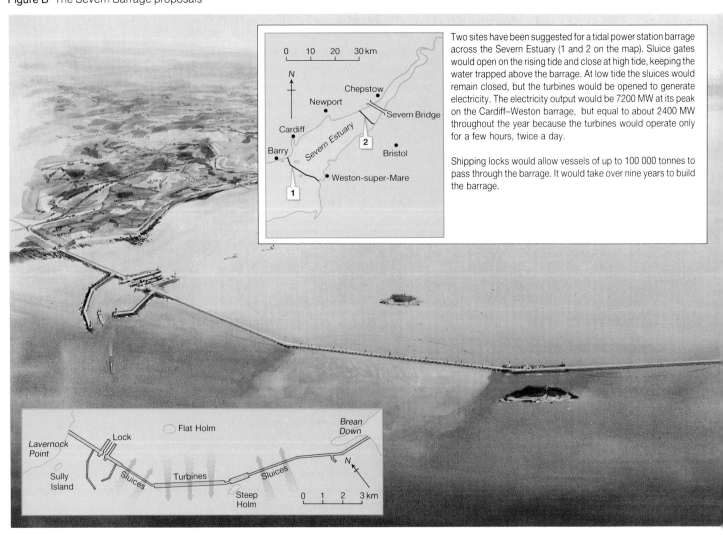

Two sites have been suggested for a tidal power station barrage across the Severn Estuary (1 and 2 on the map). Sluice gates would open on the rising tide and close at high tide, keeping the water trapped above the barrage. At low tide the sluices would remain closed, but the turbines would be opened to generate electricity. The electricity output would be 7200 MW at its peak on the Cardiff–Weston barrage, but equal to about 2400 MW throughout the year because the turbines would operate only for a few hours, twice a day.

Shipping locks would allow vessels of up to 100 000 tonnes to pass through the barrage. It would take over nine years to build the barrage.

highest tidal range at almost 16m. The Annapolis Royal tidal power station generates 20 MW of electricity. It is a pilot plant for a proposed 4800 MW giant tidal power station across the Bay of Fundy itself. There are also small experimental tidal power stations in the USSR and China.

There are also plans for tidal power stations in Britain. The most advanced plans concern the Severn Estuary which has the world's second highest tidal range (over 15 m at Chepstow). Two separate proposals have been considered by the Severn Tidal Power Group (Figure B). The smaller English Stones barrage would generate 972 MW. The larger Cardiff–Weston barrage would generate 7200 MW. The Group has recommended the latter.

A second proposal has been made for a tidal barrage across the River Mersey

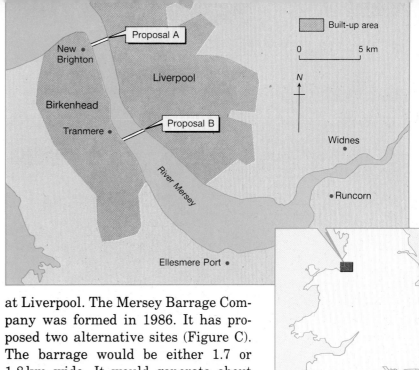

at Liverpool. The Mersey Barrage Company was formed in 1986. It has proposed two alternative sites (Figure C). The barrage would be either 1.7 or 1.8 km wide. It would generate about 500 MW of electricity on the ebb tide only. Locks would allow large ships to pass through the barrage. The Mersey Barrage is seen as a valuable source of employment in the construction phase. Up to 5000 jobs will be provided in an area of high unemployment. It could also provide new opportunities for tourism and for water sports.

Figure C The Mersey Barrage proposals

Advantages of the barrage
1 A reliable supply of cheap electricity.
2 The Bristol Channel could be used for recreation. At present it is too dangerous.
3 Jobs: 44 000 construction workers and 500 permanent staff, plus work for the engineering industry.
4 Tourism: over 700 000 tourists visit the Rance Barrage every year.
5 Increased numbers of birds and fish in the quieter waters above the barrage.

Problems
1 Very expensive.
2 Sewage and industrial effluent is at present disposed of in the estuary. Expensive extra treatment may be needed. Power station cooling systems will need changes.
3 The salmon fisheries of the Usk and Wye may be threatened.
4 The loss of tidal mudflats would affect wading birds.

QUESTIONS

1 a) Where is the world's largest operational tidal power station?
b) How much electricity does it generate?

2 Name three countries where there are experimental tidal power stations.

3 Name two estuaries in Britain where proposals have been made for the construction of tidal power stations.

4 a) Where is the Severn Estuary?
b) Why is the Severn Estuary a suitable site for a tidal power station?
c) How would the Severn Barrage generate electricity?
d) What would the peak electrical output be?
e) Why would the overall output of electricity be only one-third of the peak output?

5 Describe the advantages of the Severn Barrage under the headings (i) electricity supply (ii) employment (iii) tourism and recreation.

6 What problems would be posed by the construction of a Severn Barrage?

7 Do you think that the Severn Barrage should be built? Give your reasons.

Figure A The Burgar Hill wind turbine

On a hill on an island off the coast of Scotland stands the world's most powerful windmill. This is Burgar Hill in the Orkney Islands. The windmill is an aero-generator, or wind turbine. Completed in 1987, it has a capacity of 3 MW of electricity, enough for about 2000 homes.

The steel and glass fibre blades of the 60 metres diameter rotor complete a revolution in under two seconds. The tips of the blades travel at nearly 400 kmph. As the windspeed increases the load on the blades also increases and the tips have to be 'feathered' (turned into the wind) to limit the rotor's speed. At a windspeed of 100 kmph the tips are turned to act as air brakes, stopping the rotor to avoid damage. The rotor speed is controlled by a computer.

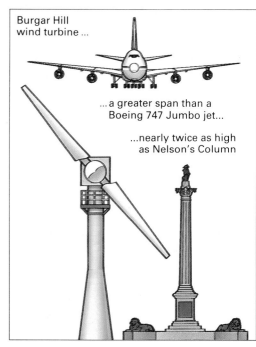

Burgar Hill wind turbine ...

...a greater span than a Boeing 747 Jumbo jet...

...nearly twice as high as Nelson's Column

Figure B The Burgar Hill wind turbine is BIG

Wind power offers a cheap, clean form of alternative energy for the future. It has been claimed that wind turbines can generate electricity 30 per cent cheaper than nuclear power stations. It sounds too good to be true. It is! There are problems which will mean that wind power alone will not be the answer to our future energy needs.

For a start, wind turbines produce their maximum output for only about a quarter of the time they are in operation. It would need over 1000 3 MW wind turbines to replace just one 1800 MW coal-fired power station! To overcome this problem it has been proposed that 'wind farms' consisting of hundreds of wind turbines could be built. A wind farm consisting of five hundred wind turbines would cover 30 square kilometres, about the same area as the city of Worcester. A wind farm like this would generate only 1 per cent of Britain's electricity needs.

Wind turbines are a clean form of energy, but they make a great impact on the landscape. The noise of hundreds of turbines would be a problem. It seems hopeless, but wind farms of nearly 17000 small wind turbines already exist in California, USA, generating up to 1500 MW. It would not be easy to obtain planning permission to build wind farms in Britain. For this reason proposals have been made to build wind farms offshore. The best sites would be at least 10 km offshore in areas where the sea is less than 20 m deep. Morecambe Bay, the southern North Sea, the eastern English Channel and the Bristol Channel have been suggested as suitable sites. Unfortunately, offshore wind turbines would be much more expensive to build and maintain than those on land.

The Burgar Hill wind turbine will be carefully monitored, together with other experimental turbines at Richborough in Kent and Carmarthen Bay in Wales. If they succeed in producing cheap electricity and are reliable in service, then five wind farms will be built by 1992, two in England, two in

Scotland and one in Wales. If these are successful then offshore wind farms may become a reality, but this would not be until well into the next century. Until then wind turbines will be most valuable as sources of electricity on offshore islands which have to depend on expensive diesel power stations.

Figure C A wind farm in California – the shape of things to come in Britain?

QUESTIONS

1 Describe the windmill shown in Figure A.

2 What are the advantages of wind power?

3 a) What is a wind farm?
  b) Why are wind farms necessary?

4 a) What problems would be created by wind farms inland?
  b) How might these problems be overcome?

5 a) Why is wind power unlikely to produce a large share of Britain's electricity in the near future?
  b) What would have to happen to make wind power more attractive?
  c) In 1987 the British government spent approximately £5 million on wind power. Do you think that more should be spent? Give your reasons.

Figure A The Sun

Electricity from the Sun

The Sun drenches the Earth with thousands of times more energy than its human inhabitants consume. If we could tap a tiny fraction of this solar energy we could meet all our energy needs with a clean, free and everlasting form of energy. Unfortunately, using solar energy on a large scale is very expensive.

You may have a calculator or watch which is solar-powered. They work through special power cells made of silicon. Silicon converts about 15 per cent of incoming sunlight into electricity.

Solar cells were developed for use on spacecraft. They are very expensive to make because they need large crystals of pure silicon which have to be grown slowly in a laboratory. Diamond-tipped saws slice the crystals into wafers, wasting at least half of the material in the process. A single 750 mm-diameter cell produces a maximum output of half a watt. Cells are usually mounted on a panel, wired together and covered with glass. It would take 5000 cells to supply a single British home with electricity.

In the early 1970s solar cell electricity cost over a hundred times more than electricity generated by coal or nuclear power stations. By 1988 the cost had fallen tremendously, but solar cell electricity is still nearly ten times more expensive than conventional methods. Despite this, experimental solar cell power stations have been built, including a 30 kilowatt unit near Southampton. The world's largest solar power station is a 10 MW giant at Daggett, California.

Small-scale solar power stations using battery banks provide energy for a wide variety of uses. They have been applied to electric fences, pumps, navigation beacons, railway points and low-intensity lighting systems.

Ever since the 1960s scientists have claimed that cheap solar power is just around the corner. In the late 1980s there seems to be some justification for these claims. The recent development of new methods of making solar cells using less pure silicon offers a big cut in costs. The cells can be made thinner and are therefore cheaper.

Solar heating

Many British homes have solar panels on their roofs which heat water. The water is fed through pipes across a black material which absorbs heat. The panel is covered by glass which prevents the heat being lost. During sunny summer days the solar panels can supply all the hot water needed. Figure D shows how building design can make better use of solar heating.

Figure B How a solar cell power system works

Solar radiation

Array of solar cells convert sunlight into electricity

Battery bank   Control unit   Solar panels

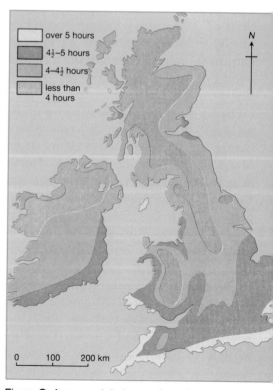

over 5 hours
4½–5 hours
4–4½ hours
less than 4 hours

N

0   100   200 km

Figure C Average daily hours of sunshine across the British Isles

A place in the sun

Direct solar power requires no expensive amplifiers or silicon cells. It simply means designing buildings as solar collectors so that they are natural sun traps. Put at its simplest, direct solar power means redistributing the glass in a house so that as much solar energy as possible is admitted on the south side, and as little as possible leaks away to the north. Scientists at the Department of Energy claim that a saving in energy bills of £50 a year can be obtained. The evidence comes from over 100 homes built on this basis in Milton Keynes.

Figure D Extract (*far left*)

Figure E (*below left*) Solar panels for water heating on the roofs of houses in London

Figure F (*left*) The Milton Keynes Energy Park

Figure G Extract (*below*)

Energy from the skies over Milton Keynes

Sun and wind energy will be used to provide domestic electricity to nine houses in an experiment at the new Milton Keynes 'Energy Park'. Each house will have a bank of solar arrays on the roof and the group of houses will be served by a wind generator with 10 m blades mounted on a 20 m tower.

The combined 30 000 watts output of arrays and wind generator is fed to a battery bank in a control room where the current is transformed for supplying the houses. If a combination of low wind and no sun over a period reduces the battery's ability to supply demand from the houses, they are automatically switched over to the normal mains supply.

The geography of solar power

There is a simple geographical problem with solar power. It is not equally distributed across the earth. Although most solar power devices can still work on cloudy days, they are most efficient in direct sunlight. Some areas, such as the deserts, have many more hours of sunshine per year than cloudier areas like the UK. Even in the UK there are great differences in sunshine amounts (Figure C). Bournemouth has an average of 1730 hours of sunshine per year, while Braemar in Scotland has only 1110 hours per year. Average sunshine amounts for Saudi Arabia are around 3000 hours per year.

If solar power really is the energy of the future, the UK and many other developed countries are going to be at a severe disadvantage. Figure F shows what the future may hold for British homes.

QUESTIONS

1. a) What are solar power cells made of?
   b) Name some everyday uses of such solar cells.
   c) Why are solar cells very expensive to make?

2. Study Figure B and say how a solar cell power system works.

3. a) What is the purpose of solar panels like those in Figure E?
   b) How do the solar panels work?

4. Read the newspaper article in Figure D. Design a three-bedroomed house that can make use of direct solar power. Draw a plan and a three-dimensional view of the house. Write a short note explaining the benefits of your design.

5. Study Figure C.
   a) Describe the pattern of sunshine amounts in the British Isles.
   b) Where would be the best areas to use solar power?

6. Study Figure G.
   a) Where is this experiment taking place?
   b) What is the average daily sunshine at this city? (See Figure C.)
   c) How many houses are involved in the experiment?
   d) How will the houses receive their electricity?
   e) What will happen when conditions are unsuitable for solar or wind power?
   f) Why does this experiment show 'what the future may hold for British homes'?

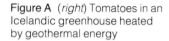

3.10 Alternatives: geothermal power

Figure A (*right*) Tomatoes in an Icelandic greenhouse heated by geothermal energy

Tomatoes ripening in a greenhouse (Figure A). Not an unusual sight until you realize that these tomatoes are growing in Iceland, near the Arctic Circle, and the greenhouse gets its heat from deep within the earth. Boreholes have been sunk 650 m underground. Hot water at a temperature of 86°C rises to the surface at a rate of over 20 000 litres per minute. This is geothermal energy.

The earth is an enormous nuclear reactor. Heat generated by radioactive decay in the molten core of the planet flows through the ground and out into space. Tapping a small fraction of this heat could supply all the human race's energy needs. In some places this is already happening.

Almost all the buildings in the Icelandic capital, Reykjavik, are heated by geothermal water. Iceland is a volcanic island, sited on the Mid-Atlantic Ridge. This is a boundary zone between two vast plates of the earth's crust. The plates are moving slowly apart and molten rock is rising from deep underground to fill the gap. Geothermal heat is used in several other volcanic areas, including New Zealand and Italy.

There are some areas where high temperature geothermal steam can be tapped. This can be used to spin turbines to generate electricity. There are a number of small geothermal electric power stations in Iceland, but there are much larger plants in Italy at Larderello in Tuscany (Figure B). This was the world's first geothermal power station when it started operations in 1913. Today it produces 400 MW of electricity. A larger plant in California, USA, produces 500 MW from over a hundred boreholes. The plant is at a site called The Geysers, some 150 km north of San Francisco.

Figure B The geothermal power station at Larderello, Italy

Geothermal energy in the UK

There are several hot springs in the UK, those at Bath in Avon being the most famous. Research in the 1980s by the Department of Energy concluded that it would be too expensive to use this water for heating or for generating electricity, but it remains a possibility for the future. The city of Southampton has gone ahead with a small geothermal heating scheme, despite the withdrawal of support from the Department of Energy (Figure C). This may be the first of several similar schemes.

Over £25 million has been spent by the Department of Energy and the European Community on a large experiment at Camborne in Cornwall. This is using the 'hot, dry rock' method of generating geothermal electricity. Two boreholes, each 2800 m deep, have been sunk beneath the Rosemanoes quarry to a geothermally heated zone of granite. Cold water is pumped down one borehole and hot water at temperatures between 70°C and 90°C returns up the second borehole (Figure D). A turbo-generator at the surface produces 5 MW of electricity. Unfortunately the experiment has hit snags. Sometimes little of

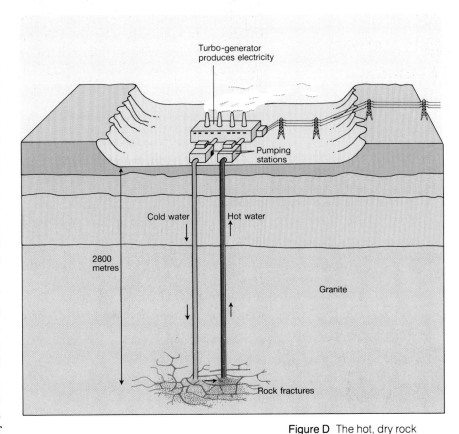

Figure D The hot, dry rock method of tapping geothermal energy

the water pumped down returns to the surface. The study team want to drill deeper boreholes down to below 6000 m. They believe that these will produce water at 180°C.

Should the Camborne project succeed it holds out the hope of producing cheap, inexhaustible and continuous energy from many areas underlain by igneous rock. Geothermal energy has much promise as an alternative energy source of the future.

Figure C Extract

Geothermal heat to serve British city

Southampton is to become the first city in Britain to be heated by hot water from hundreds of metres underground.

A group of city-centre buildings, including the Town Hall, will be supplied with the heat by a French company that runs similar schemes on the Continent.

Under the agreements, Southampton Civic Centre, the Institute of Higher Education and a leading department store will be heated with water brought to the surface at 74°C from 1800 metres below the city. Planning permission has been given for a wellhead installation in a car park, pumps and control rooms at a nearby heat station and a network of pipes to distribute the heat.

QUESTIONS

1 a) What is geothermal heat? How is it created?
   b) Why is Iceland an area of geothermal heat?
   c) How has Iceland used its geothermal resources?

2 How can geothermal energy be used to generate electricity?

3 a) Name the first British city to be heated by geothermal water.
   b) Describe the scheme.

4 a) What is meant by the 'hot, dry rock' method of generating geothermal electricity?
   b) Where have experiments been carried out into this method in Britain?
   c) Copy Figure D and explain how the method works.

A Public Enquiry has been called to consider the application by the Central Electricity Generating Board (CEGB) to build a nuclear power station at Hinkley Point in Somerset (Figure A). The simulation which follows is based on the actual submissions to the earlier Sizewell B Public Enquiry.

Figures A–F are all submissions to the Public Planning Enquiry, called to consider the CEGB's application to build a nuclear power station at Hinkley Point. Figure G is a newspaper extract, based on an article in *The Guardian*, 27 October 1987

Submission to the Public Planning Enquiry from the Central Electricity Generating Board:

The Board applies for permission to build a Pressurized Water Nuclear Reactor (PWR) at Hinkley Point, Somerset. Construction would begin in 1990 for a completion date of 1997. Our confidence in the safety of the PWR was thoroughly vindicated at the enquiry into the Sizewell B reactor after a long and rigorous examination. We predict the need for ten PWRs by the year 2000.

The site of Hinkley Point has several advantages for the construction of a PWR:

★ a large, flat site with firm foundations
★ an ample supply of cooling water from the Bristol Channel, so cooling towers will not be required
★ it is in the right place to help balance electricity supply in the South-West
★ new electricity transmission lines will not be needed
★ the Board already owns the site, and there are already two older nuclear power stations located there (Hinkley Point A and B)

The Hinkley Point PWR will bring many advantages to the local and national economy:

★ 10 000 jobs would be created during the construction phase
★ 90 per cent of construction work would go to UK companies
★ £300 million would be injected into the local economy
★ by-passes will be constructed for Bridgewater and Cannington; the Board will make a substantial contribution to their cost
★ it will help keep the cost of electricity as low as possible
★ it will reduce the Board's over-reliance upon coal as a fuel

The decision to proceed with Hinkley Point C should be made as swiftly as posssible in the national interest.

Figure A

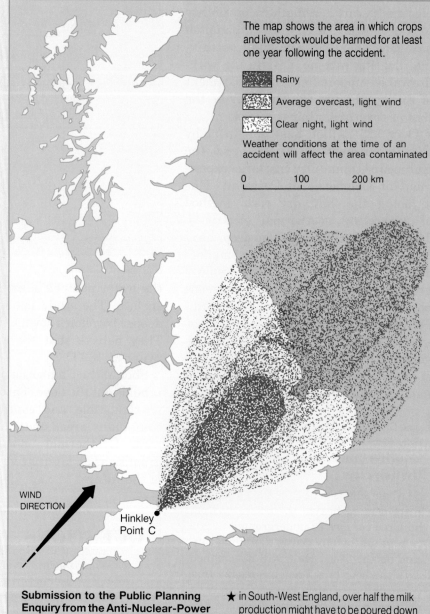

The map shows the area in which crops and livestock would be harmed for at least one year following the accident.

Rainy

Average overcast, light wind

Clear night, light wind

Weather conditions at the time of an accident will affect the area contaminated

0   100   200 km

WIND DIRECTION

Hinkley Point C

Submission to the Public Planning Enquiry from the Anti-Nuclear-Power Group:

Based on the experience of the Chernobyl nuclear disaster, we have prepared a report showing the likely effects of an accident at the proposed Hinkley Point PWR. The main points of the report are:

★ a quarter of the UK's annual farm crops might have to be destroyed because of radioactive contamination

★ in South-West England, over half the milk production might have to be poured down the drain
★ in some areas farmland might have to be abandoned for up to fifty years
★ between 30 and 40 people would be killed soon after the accident
★ several thousands would die due to cancers from radioactivity over the thirty years following the accident

Figure B

Submission to the Public Planning Enquiry from the Allied Union of Powerworkers:

The UK nuclear power programme has a safety record which is second to none. We have complete confidence in PWR design. We support the application to construct a PWR at Hinkley Point. It will provide continuity of employment for our members who would otherwise face redundancy when Hinkley Point A closes in the mid–1990s.

Figure C

Submission to the Public Planning Enquiry from Somerset County Council:

We object to the proposal to build a PWR at Hinkley Point. Our objections are based on the following grounds:

★ we are seriously concerned about the safety of the PWR design. There have been serious breakdowns of the existing two nuclear power stations at Hinkley Point
★ this scenically beautiful part of West Somerset already has more than its fair share of the nuclear power industry
★ the infrastructure of the area is not suited to major building projects. Small country roads are incapable of taking the construction traffic

Figure D

Submission to the Public Planning Enquiry from Friends of the Earth:

We object strongly to the proposal to build a PWR at Hinkley Point. The application is a gross misuse of public funds. It bears all the hallmark of an institution which is utterly unresponsive to public opinion and totally beyond public control. Following the nuclear disaster at Chernobyl, it is quite clear that the British public does not want and will not tolerate any more nuclear power stations. The CEGB is behaving more like a public menace than a public servant.

★ nuclear power is dangerous — both in the short and long term
★ nuclear power is expensive — coal-fired stations are cheaper to build
★ nuclear power is unnecessary — coal-fired stations are still being closed, alternative energy sources should be developed

Figure E

FOR TWENTY YEARS the CEGB said that nuclear electricity was cheaper than coal and that without it fuel bills would rise. Lord Marshall (head of the CEGB) does not dispute that the CEGB's own figures now show that over the lifetime of the power station, the early nuclear power stations generate electricity which is 7 per cent more expensive than coal.

Figure G

Submission to the Public Planning Enquiry from the directors of Power Construction (UK) plc:

It is vital that a decision be taken to proceed with Hinkley Point C as soon as possible. The jobs of 500 people at our Manchester factory are dependent upon this order. We believe that Hinkley Point C will be £200 million cheaper than the Sizewell B PWR because of economies of scale and lessons learned. We are confident that Hinkley Point C design will attract many export orders.

Figure F

QUESTIONS

1 a) Read Figure A carefully. Make sure that you understand it.
  b) Write down the main points of the application from the CEGB.
  c) Read Figure G.

2 You are going to take the part of one of the interested parties at the Public Enquiry.
  a) Join with others to form a small group. You will be representing the views of one of the following parties:
    (i) the CEGB
    (ii) Somerset County Council
    (iii) Friends of the Earth
    (iv) the Anti-Nuclear-Power Group
    (v) the Allied Union of Powerworkers
    (vi) Power Construction (UK) plc
  b) Each member of your group should take on the role of representing one of these parties. The role which you adopt depends upon your surname. The roles are to be taken from (i) to (vi) in alphabetical order of your surnames.
  c) Each member should write down the main points of the party which they have to represent (Figures A to F).

3 Your group should then carry out the Public Enquiry.
  a) Each member of the group should have the chance to make a short presentation of their case. The representative of the CEGB should start.
  b) After each presentation, the other members should be allowed to ask questions.

4 After a Public Enquiry a final decision is made by an inspector who has been listening to the cases presented by each of the parties. You should now take on the role of that inspector.
  a) Working on your own, think about what was said at the Enquiry. Make a list of the advantages and disadvantages of building Hinkley Point C.
  b) Make a final decision on the application. Here are some of the decisions which you could make:
    (i) The plan, as it now is, should be approved.
    (ii) The plan should be changed in some ways.
    (iii) The plan should be rejected.
  c) Write a short report outlining your decision and giving your reasons for your decision.

5 The decisions of the whole class should be recorded.
  a) What was the majority decision?
  b) What were the main reasons for this decision?
  c) How many people opposed the majority decision?
  d) What were their main reasons for opposing the majority decision?

Unit 3 ASSESSMENT

1 Study Figure A showing energy consumption in France in 1973 and 1986.

a) In which year was most energy consumed?
(1 mark)

b) Name, in order of importance, the three main sources of energy in both of the years shown. (3 marks)

c) Which source of energy increased its share of the total by the largest amount between 1973 and 1986?
(2 marks)

d) Which source of energy decreased its share of the total by the largest amount between 1973 and 1986?
(2 marks)

e) Give one reason for the changes affecting the share of the total provided by (i) oil and (ii) nuclear energy.
(4 marks)

Figure A Sources of energy consumed in France, 1973 and 1986

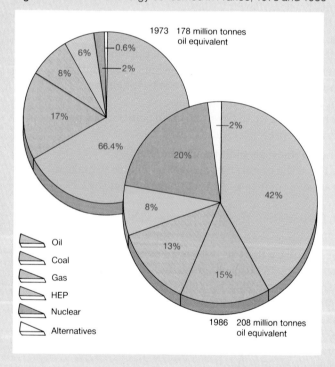

2 Study Figure B (right).

a) Draw a bar graph to illustrate these statistics.
(8 marks)

b) Name the four leading electricity producing nations in Western Europe.
(2 marks)

c) Why do these four nations produce so much more electricity than the other West European nations?
(3 marks)

3 Figure C shows the location of major fossil-fuel power stations in England and Wales.

a) Name the two main fuels used in the fossil-fuel power stations.
(2 marks)

b) Briefly describe the location of the power stations shown on the map.
(3 marks)

c) Give three reasons for the location you have described.
(6 marks)

Figure C The location of fossil-fuel power stations in England and Wales

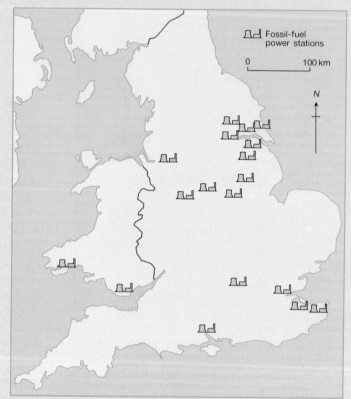

Figure B The ten major electricity producing nations in Western Europe

Country	Electricity produced (thousand million kWh)
Belgium	53
France	284
Italy	183
Netherlands	60
Norway	106
Spain	116
Sweden	110
Switzerland	52
UK	276
West Germany	374

4 Figure D shows a nuclear power station.
   a) Give one piece of evidence from the photograph which shows that this power station is nuclear.
   (1 mark)
   b) Give two reasons shown on the photograph why this was a good site for a nuclear power station.
   (4 marks)
   c) Give two arguments for, and two against, an increase in the number of nuclear power stations in the UK.
   (8 marks)

5 a) Consider the following sources of energy: (i) tidal (ii) wind (iii) solar. For each give one advantage and one disadvantage as a source of energy in the UK.
   (6 marks)
   b) What is geothermal heat? (1 mark)
   c) How does a geothermal power station generate electricity?
   (4 marks)

   TOTAL: 60 marks

Figure D The Bradwell nuclear power station

Details for pupil profile sheet Unit 3

Knowledge and understanding

1 Uneven distribution of the world's energy resources
2 Growing dependence of developed world upon resources of developing countries
3 Varying energy consumption rates between developed and developing countries
4 Energy conservation
5 Changing patterns of energy use
6 The oil crisis of 1973–74
7 Fossil fuel
8 Electricity generation
9 Nuclear power
10 Alternatives: tidal, wind, solar and geothermal

Skills

1 Interpreting data from tables
2 Interpreting topological maps
3 Interpreting line graphs
4 Draw a pie graph
5 Draw a flow chart
6 Writing script for television news report
7 Designing an advertising poster
8 Considering different views before reaching a decision
9 Role play

Values

1 Awareness of the problems of nuclear waste disposal
2 Detecting bias in advertising
3 Concern for the quality of the environment

Unit 4: Water

Water has been called the universal raw material. All industries use water All types of farming use water. All life uses water. Water is vital, yet many people in the developed world take water for granted. Water is always available at the turn of a tap. Without water our domestic life would collapse and disease would threaten our lives. Factories and farms would fall into disuse. Where does the water come from? Fortunately, water is a renewable resource.

We live on a planet of water (Figure A). Nearly 70 per cent of the surface area of Earth is water. However, very little of this water is of any direct use to people. Over 97 per cent of the earth's water is salt water in the oceans. Most of the freshwater is stored in ice caps. Only a tiny fraction is easily available for people to use in rivers, lakes and rocks (Figure C). Yet there is still plenty of freshwater to go around. World consumption is estimated at 4000 cubic kilometres per year. This is only about 2 per cent of the amount of water available in rivers and lakes, and only 10 per cent of the yearly runoff of water back to the sea. So why do so many people in the world go thirsty? Like most natural resources, water is

Figure A Earth from space. The Atlantic Ocean is clearly visible, the Indian Ocean and vast Pacific Ocean lie on the other side of the globe

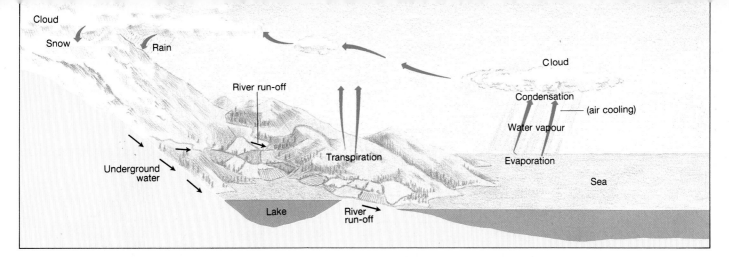

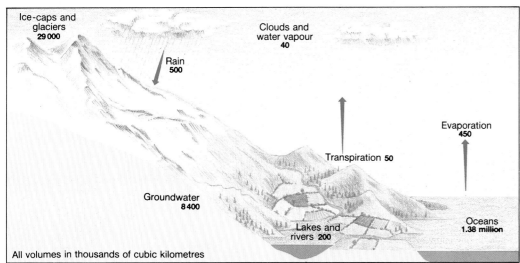

Figure B (*above*) The hydrological cycle

Ice-caps and glaciers **29 000**

Clouds and water vapour **40**

Rain **500**

Evaporation **450**

Transpiration **50**

Groundwater **8 400**

Lakes and rivers **200**

Oceans **1.38 million**

All volumes in thousands of cubic kilometres

Figure C Water storage in the hydrological cycle

not evenly distributed around the earth. Some places have too much, others have too little.

Although water is a renewable resource it is possible for people to over-exploit water and reduce supplies. This can happen if too much water is extracted from a river or lake. However, the water cycle is a rapid process. On average it takes 14 days for water to return to the oceans from which it came. Much more serious is over-exploitation of groundwater supplies because these may take many centuries to be renewed. This has happened in the case of London. Underground water provides 10 per cent of London's current water, but the amount has been falling in recent years. Centuries ago the water gushed up to the surface under its own pressure through artesian wells. Now the artesian effect has been lost because of over-use and the water has to be pumped to the surface. There are fears that the wells may soon dry up.

QUESTIONS

1 a) Make a list of the ways you have used water today.
b) Does your use of water change with the seasons? If so, how?

2 Copy the systems diagram of the hydrological cycle below and complete it using Figure B to help you.

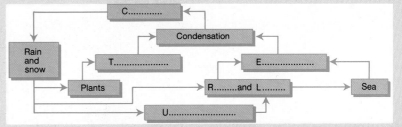

3 a) What percentage of Earth's surface area consists of water?
b) What percentage of the earth's water is salty?

4 a) Where is most of the earth's freshwater stored?
b) What is the world's annual consumption of freshwater?
c) How much of the water available in rivers and lakes is consumed by people?

5 'The earth has plenty of freshwater, yet millions of people go thirsty.' Explain this statement.

6 How does London's water supply illustrate the dangers of over-exploitation of water resources?

Rain stopped play... again! It always seems to be raining in Britain. But does it really rain so much? The table below might surprise you:

Figure A Rainfall frequency in Britain

Place	Hours of rain per year	Percentage of the time it is raining
London	506	5.8
Leeds	552	6.3
Swansea	696	7.9
Glasgow	876	10.0

Even in Glasgow there are nine dry hours for every one wet hour.

But there is no doubt that Britain has plenty of water. The trouble is that most of it falls over the mountains of Wales, northern England and Scotland, where few people live and demand for water is low. The regions with the greatest demand for water are the east and south of England. They do not have enough water to supply their demands. These are the driest regions of the country and also the warmest and sunniest, with the highest evaporation rates.

Figure B A quick run ... to the pavilion!

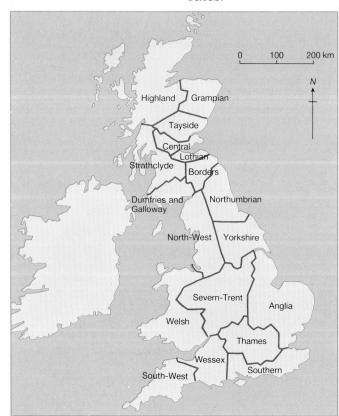

Figure C Regional Water Authorities in Britain

Annual rainfall (millimetres)

- more than 2500
- 1500–2500
- 750–1500
- 500–750

0   100   200   300

Figure D Rainfall distribution in the British Isles

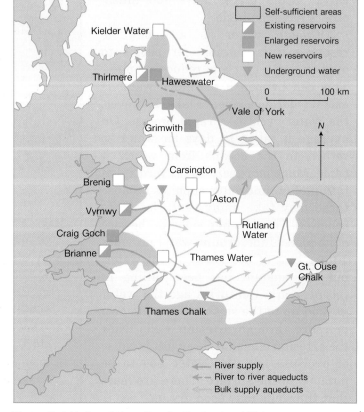

- Self-sufficient areas
- Existing reservoirs
- Enlarged reservoirs
- New reservoirs
- Underground water

0   100 km

- ← River supply
- ← River to river aqueducts
- ← Bulk supply aqueducts

Figure E A National Water Plan for England and Wales

Britain's water supplies are managed by the regional water authorities shown in Figure C. They are responsible for:

- water treatment and supply
- sewage treatment and disposal
- land drainage
- flood prevention
- pollution control
- managing fishing and boating

The transfer of water from the surplus areas of the north and west to the deficit areas of the south and east is a complex and expensive task. A network of pumphouses, treatment works, reservoirs and pipes is needed. In the 1970s a National Water Plan for England and Wales introduced the idea of a 'water grid'. Although the Plan has not been accepted by the government, parts of it have already been developed including the Kielder Water and Rutland Water reservoirs. Schemes have been proposed to build barrages to store water in Morecambe Bay, the Wash, and the Dee and Severn estuaries. Such schemes could have serious effects upon wildlife and the environment. The growth in demand for water has slowed down since the early 1970s and new schemes no longer seem so vital. The present system, largely regional with little national co-ordination, will continue for the forseeable future.

Figure F Average daily use of water per person in Britain and Bangladesh

Use of water	Amount used daily (litres)	
	Britain	Rural Bangladesh
Washing	50	13
Flushing toilet	50	0
Cooking and drinking	6	6
Washing dishes and cleaning	18	5
Washing clothes	20	11
Watering garden	10	0
Washing car	3	0
Others	23	10
Total	180	45

Sources of water supply in Britain

There are four main sources of water supply in Britain:

Rivers

Rivers provide the main source of water supply throughout Britain. The water is usually pumped into open storage reservoirs before being treated and supplied to the water system. Most of London's water is taken from the rivers Thames and Lea. There are several large open storage reservoirs beside both rivers. At Staines there are eight reservoirs including the giant Queen Mary Reservoir which is over twice the size of Hyde Park.

Wells

Permeable rocks such as chalk, limestone and sandstone are called *aquifers* because they bear water. The water can be pumped out through wells. About ten per cent of London's water is supplied by wells.

Springs

Springs occur where an aquifer overlies an impermeable rock. The water travels along the aquifer and emerges as a spring, often at the foot of a hill. Spring water contains dissolved minerals which have some medicinal value. It became fashionable to 'take the waters' of springs during the eighteenth century. A number of towns called spas grew up near large springs, such as Cheltenham, Buxton, Bath and Droitwich.

Reservoirs

Reservoirs have been built in the upland areas of Britain to store river water which would otherwise flow into the sea. The amount of water released into the river can then be controlled. Reservoir schemes have faced tremendous criticism.

QUESTIONS

1 'Britain has plenty of water. The trouble is that most of it falls where demand for water is low.' Explain this statement.

2 a) How many regional water authorities are there in Britain?
   b) What are the authorities responsible for?

3 What is an aquifer? Name an example.

4 What is (a) a spring (b) a spa?

5 a) What are the main features of the National Water Plan?
   b) Why has the plan not been accepted by the government?

6 Estuary storage sites are possible new sources of water supply. What problems do you think will be created by developing them? (Think of the effects on wildlife, tidal mudflats, shipping, fishing and so on.)

7 Figure F shows the average daily use of water by each person in Britain and compares it with the average daily use by each person in rural Bangladesh.

   a) Draw two divided bars to illustrate these statistics. Let 1 mm represent 1 litre. The bar for Britain should be 180 mm long; the bar for Bangladesh should be 45 mm long.
   b) (i) Name three uses of water in Britain which do not exist in rural Bangladesh.
      (ii) Explain why these three uses do not exist in rural Bangladesh.

The road leads through the pine forest, dark and brooding. Norway fir, spruce and larch line the roadside, retreating in ranks into the gloom. Sunlight filters fleetingly through the densely-planted trees. Through the trees ahead there is a glimpse of gold. Suddenly the road bursts out of the forest and you are driving along a lakeside, the deep blue water stretching as far as you can see in either direction. This is not Norway or Sweden, but Northumberland in North-East England.

Figure A Kielder Water, with the main recreation centre at Leaplish in the foreground

Kielder Water is the largest reservoir in Britain. It is 12 km long and covers an area of 1086 hectares. The reservoir stores 188 000 million litres of water. It is the lynchpin of a regional water grid. This great scheme cost £170 million, £60 million of which was given in the form of grants by the EC Regional Development Fund and the British government. A further £43 million was loaned by the EC at reduced rates of interest.

The giant dam, 1140 m long and 52 m high, was built upstream of the village of Falstone. This is one of the narrowest points in the valley and the gradient of the River North Tyne upstream of this point is fairly gentle, allowing a large reservoir to build up behind the dam. The reservoir was officially opened in 1982. One and a half million trees were felled to make way for it, and a hamlet, several buildings and the main valley road were drowned by the rising water.

Kielder was planned in the early 1970s when the North-East's demand for water was growing rapidly (Figure B). It will supply up to 1130 million litres of water a day. Kielder is a regional scheme because its water will be available to almost all parts of the North-East (Figure D). Water released from Kielder Dam flows for 58 km down river to Riding Mill where a pumping station transfers water from the Tyne to the Wear and Tees through a 38 km long aqueduct, most of which is in the form of a tunnel.

A multi-purpose project

The main purpose of Kielder Water is water supply. However, such great projects are now usually built with several purposes in mind.

Tourism. Caravan and camp sites, forest cabins and outdoor activity centres have been built. There are forest walks, picnic places and viewpoints. The Kielder Water Visitor Centre provides information and restaurant facilities. Water sports are encouraged, pleasure boat trips and ferry services are run.

Angling. The reservoir has been stocked with 250 000 brown trout and fishing permits are sold to the public.

Nature reserve. Bakethin Reservoir has been set aside as a nature reserve. Heron, curlew, kestrel and short-eared owl are amongst the birds to be seen here.

Hydro-electricity. Two turbo-alternators have been installed at the dam to produce up to six megawatts of electricity which is supplied to the national grid.

A white elephant

When the Kielder Water plans were first considered, there was opposition from local people. Some were directly affected by the loss of buildings and

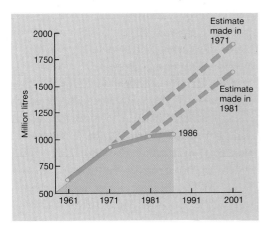

Figure B Daily water consumption in North-East England, 1961–2001

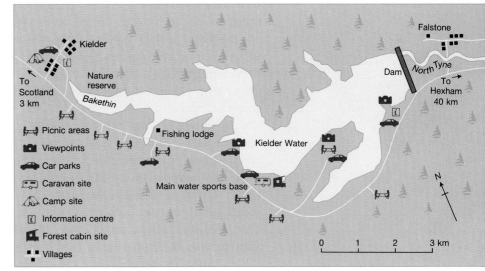

Figure C (*above*) Kielder Water

Figure D The regional supply of water from Kielder

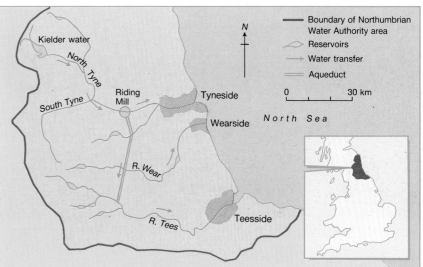

farmland. Others were upset by the threatened transformation of a peaceful forested valley. There was also opposition from some conservationists who feared that the reservoir would alter the wildlife habitats and attract too many tourists into the area.

As stated earlier, Kielder was planned at a time when the North-East's water demands were rapidly increasing. Since the mid-1970s the rate of increase has declined. The collapse of industry on Teesside has been mainly responsible. For example, the British Steel Corporation reserved 160 million litres a day in 1974 but by the 1980s it was using only 25 million litres.

The planners would not have believed it back in the 1970s, but Kielder Water's main function now is as a centre for tourism. Its water is not really needed in the North-East at present. Some has even been exported by tanker to the Middle East! The expense of the scheme has placed Northumbrian Water heavily in debt.

Within the space of ten years, a remote and beautiful Northumberland valley has been transformed. Jobs have been provided for local people. A major new tourist centre has been established and the demand for water in the North-East has been safeguarded into the next century.

QUESTIONS

1 a) Where is Kielder Water?
   b) What is its area?
   c) How much water does it store?

2 What were the advantages of the site of Kielder for a reservoir?

3 a) Why was Kielder Water built?
   b) Which areas use the water from Kielder?
   c) How is the water supplied to those areas?

4 Why is Kielder Water an example of a multi-purpose project?

5 Design a publicity pamphlet for the Northumbrian Water Authority aimed at informing tourists of the facilities available at Kielder Water. It should include a brief summary of the purpose and development of the scheme.

6 'The Kielder Water Scheme is unnecessary and has resulted in the loss of a valuable resource – solitude.' Discuss this statement and give your own views.

4.4 Irrigation

One of the world's greatest irrigation schemes is in Australia. A massive engineering project has brought water to an area of semi-desert and created a rich agricultural region. Figure A shows the extent of the Snowy Mountains Scheme.

Two-thirds of Australia is desert or semi-desert. Only the narrow coastal strips have high rainfall totals. The country's highest mountain range, the Great Dividing Range, runs north to south along Australia's eastern coast. The Snowy Mountains rise above 2500 m close to the border of New South Wales and Victoria. They are snow-covered for half the year and are the source area of three of Australia's mightiest rivers.

The Snowy Mountains are a watershed: the Snowy River flows eastwards to the Tasman Sea while the Murray and the Murrumbidgee flow westwards to the Great Australian Bight. The Murray and the Murrumbidgee cross the dry plains of the interior. The long, arid summer with its high rates of evaporation cause the flow of these rivers to be greatly reduced, making them unsuitable for large-scale irrigation. The Snowy Mountains Scheme aimed to boost the flow of these rivers during the summer by diverting the headwaters of the Snowy River and directing them into the Murray and Murrumbidgee. This involved driving tunnels through the mountains to turn the eastward flowing river in a westerly direction!

Begun in 1949, the Snowy Mountains Scheme was completed in 1974. The scheme includes:

- over 145 km of tunnels
- 80 km of aqueducts and irrigation canals
- sixteen dams and reservoirs
- eight hydro-electric power stations

Irrigation water is provided for over 260 000 hectares of land, increasing the irrigated area of the Murray/Murrumbidgee Plains by more than 25 per cent. Most of the water is stored during the winter months (May to August) in the Hume and Burrinjuck Reservoirs. It is released to boost supplies during the long, dry summer.

Figure A The Snowy Mountains Scheme

Figure C (*photograph*) Lake Eucumbene

Figure B (*below*) A cross-section through the Snowy-Murray Diversion

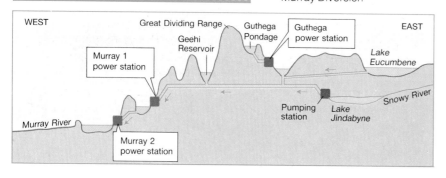

Figure D Rice farming on irrigated land around Coleambally

Figure E (*above right*) The Tumut 3 power station

Figure F (*right*) Australia's population distribution

The largest new irrigation area is Coleambally where 250 farms have been developed and a new town of over 2000 people has been built. Citrus fruit and vines are grown in this area. Elsewhere the scheme has allowed the extension of existing irrigated areas. Rice, peaches and pears are grown around Griffith and Leeton. The areas north of the River Murray are devoted to grapes, citrus fruit and temporary pastures for cattle. The Mildura/Wentworth area is a major centre for dried fruit.

The Snowy Mountains Scheme also provides hydro-electricity, 3750 megawatts of it. There are eight HEP stations which supply the needs of homes and industry in the eastern Australian cities. Most of the power is available to meet peak demand and sudden surges in demand which cannot be met by the slower-reacting fossil-fuel power stations. The Snowy Mountains power stations are well located, about half way between Sydney and Melbourne, Australia's largest markets for electricity.

A network of roads has been built, opening up this previously inaccessible area. This has boosted the Snowy Mountains' tourist industry. Summer attractions like fishing and boating are supplemented by winter sports.

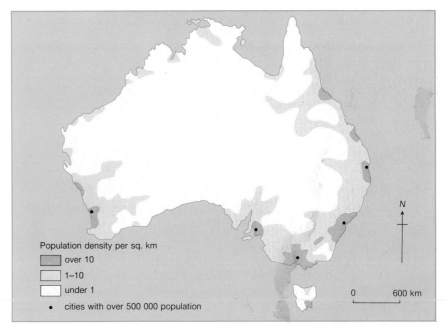

Population density per sq. km
- over 10
- 1–10
- under 1
- • cities with over 500 000 population

0   600 km

N

QUESTIONS

1 Where is the Snowy Mountains Scheme?

2 Study the map of population distribution in Australia (Figure F). Using the climate relief maps in your atlas to help you, describe and explain the population distribution of Australia.

3 Why do the Snowy Mountains provide an example of a 'watershed'?

4 a) Why are the Murray and the Murrumbidgee unsuitable for large-scale irrigation in their natural state?
   b) What was the aim of the Snowy Mountains Scheme?

5 How has the irrigation water provided by the Snowy Mountains Scheme been used?

6 How has the Snowy Mountains Scheme boosted (a) electricity production and (b) tourism?

83

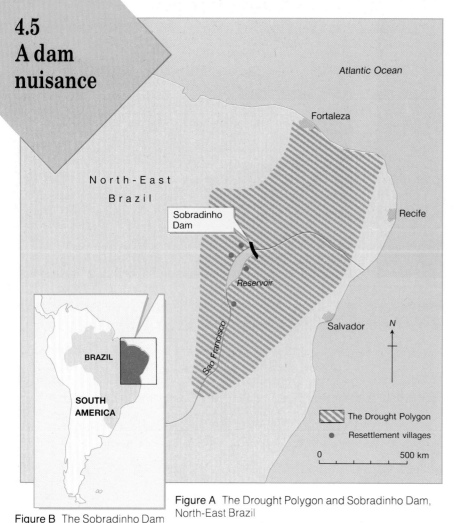

4.5
A dam nuisance

Figure A The Drought Polygon and Sobradinho Dam, North-East Brazil

Figure B The Sobradinho Dam

A reliable and safe water supply is an essential for economic development. In some areas of the world large water control and supply schemes have transformed arid, backward areas into highly productive regions. Such schemes have many advantages:

- they ensure adequate water supplies
- farmland can be irrigated and farm outputs improved
- hydro-electric power can be generated
- jobs are created in farming and industry
- the reservoirs created by dams can be useful fishing grounds and can be used for water transport

It is not surprising that water supply schemes have been very popular in the developing world. There have been many successful schemes. However, there have also been many problems when large schemes have been built in unsuitable areas.

The Sobradinho Dam

In North-East Brazil is an area known as the Drought Polygon (Figure A). The region has a savanna climate with a wet season from January to June and a dry season from July to December. The wet season is unreliable, however. Every ten years or so the rains fail and there is drought. The droughts may last for several years and often end suddenly, with downpours that cause heavy flooding.

The Drought Polygon is not a good place to make a living from farming, yet most people in the area try to do just that. They are peasant farmers growing only enough for their own needs. They have little money, so if their crops fail they face famine. In the 1870s over half a million people died in a three-year long drought. Over a hundred years later the region was equally threatened by a drought which lasted for six years between 1978 and 1984. Thousands of people died. Figures as high as three million deaths have been claimed. Yet great efforts had been made to prevent such a tragedy. It seems that some of the deaths were caused by those efforts rather than prevented by them.

A dam was built at Sobradinho on the River São Francisco. Behind the dam a large reservoir formed. It was intended to provide water to improve farming and 900 megawatts of electricity for the coastal cities of the North-East. It cost £300 million.

The reservoir formed by the Sobradinho Dam drowned the flood plain of the River São Francisco for a distance of over 300 km. Lost beneath the waters of the reservoir was some of the best farmland in the Drought Polygon. The homes of 70 000 people were destroyed. In the extract below a British journalist visiting the area describes the plight of these peoples.

Figure C A rural home, North-East Brazil

A disaster for the people

'Most of them had made a fair living as peasant farmers on well-watered, fertile soil. Many were simply thrown off their land and given no compensation, no new home or land. Those who did receive a new home in one of the resettlement villages often received no land. If they did receive land it was often several kilometres away from their new home. They had to clear the land themselves and find the money to pay for seeds and fertilizer. In many cases there was not even any water available, despite that vast reservoir nearby. The peasants were too scared to borrow money from banks. Some of the few who did borrow money found it impossible to repay the loans. The banks took their land and left them helpless.

Of course, there had been plans to resettle all the people displaced by the dam and to provide them with land on which they could make a good living. But somehow along the way the plans went wrong – corruption and greed, plus a callous indifference to the plight of these poor people, enabled the electricity company to complete only part of the resettlement scheme. The reservoir has been a disaster for the people of the Sobradinho area.'

QUESTIONS

1 Copy and complete the passage below, using the words in this list:

industry water fishing hydro- water reservoirs irrigation

> In some countries large _____ control and supply schemes have transformed backward areas into highly productive regions. Such schemes have many advantages: they supply _____ and _____ electricity, _____ water for farmland, and create jobs in both farming and _____. Behind the dams _____ form which can be used for transport and for _____.

2 What is the 'Drought Polygon'?

3 Study the climate figures below:

Climate data for a town in the Drought Polygon

Month	J	F	M	A	M	J	J	A	S	O	N	D
Temperature (°C)	29	28	27	27	26	26	27	28	28	29	29	29
Rainfall (mm)	30	50	120	105	70	50	10	5	0	0	5	10

a) What is the annual range of temperature?
b) When are the hottest months?
c) What is the total annual rainfall?
d) Draw a bar graph to illustrate the rainfall statistics.
e) What problems are created for farmers in a region with a climate like this?

4 a) On which river is the Sobradinho Dam?
   b) Why was the Sobradinho Dam built?

5 You work as a reporter for BBC Television News. You have been sent to Brazil to prepare a five-minute report on the effects of the Sobradinho Dam for the British news bulletins.
   a) Prepare a list of six scenes which you will film and include in your report.
   b) Write the script to accompany the six scenes, plus an introduction and summary to your report.
   c) If you have a tape recorder or video, record the report.

6 What do you think should have happened at Sobradinho? Who should have paid?

A huge 'barge train' carrying over 10 000 tonnes of iron ore makes its way up the River Rhine in the Netherlands. Four barges are pushed as one unit by the immensely powerful push-tow tug. The tug has three 1800 horsepower engines. This is Europe's most powerful inland waterway craft.

Inland waterways are an important means of transport in several European countries (Figure B), accounting for a considerable percentage of total freight transport in the Netherlands, Belgium and West Germany. There are several important river systems of which the Rhine, Danube, Rhone and Seine are the most important. The rivers have been straightened and deepened, and huge locks have been built to improve navigation. Vessels of over 2000 tonnes sail into the heart of Europe. Figure C shows the extensive port facilities at Basle in Switzerland. Almost a thousand kilometres from the open sea, over eight million tonnes of cargo pass through these docks each year. This

Figure A A push-tow barge train

amounts to a third of Switzerland's total foreign trade!

Inland waterways can carry bulk cargoes cheaply. Barges use much less fuel than lorries or trains. Barges are quieter and they create little pollution. They are safer than other means of transport. Inland waterway transport is slow, but speed is not important for most cargoes.

A network of deep canals has been constructed throughout Europe to link the main river systems. The inland

Figure B Freight transport by mode in six West European countries

Figure C The port of Basle

Figure D Scharnebeck barge lift

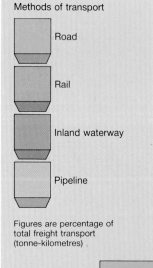

Methods of transport

Road

Rail

Inland waterway

Pipeline

Figures are percentage of total freight transport (tonne-kilometres)

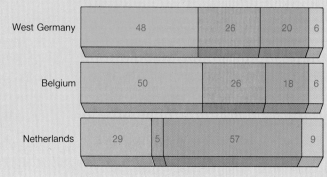

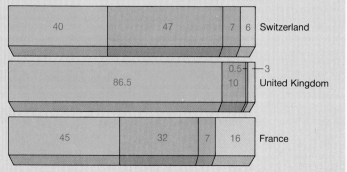

	Road	Rail	Inland waterway	Pipeline
West Germany	48	26	20	6
Belgium	50	26	18	6
Netherlands	29	5	57	9
Switzerland	40	47	7	6
United Kingdom	86.5	10	0.5	3
France	45	32	7	16

waterway system has been constantly upgraded to meet the changing demands of modern transport. Figure D shows the massive barge lift at Scharnebeck on the Elbe Lateral Canal in West Germany. This complex structure lifts fully-laden barges 38 m up a steep ridge in just a few minutes.

The craft sailing on Europe's inland waterways have also been designed to meet the changing needs. Many specialized barges have been built to transport chemicals, petroleum products, vehicles and containers. Economies of scale have been achieved by the introduction of push-tow barges. Push-tow barges now make up 15 per cent of the total fleet of inland waterway craft in the EC. Specially designed sea-going ships with shallow draughts and low superstructures are able to sail far inland.

Inland waterways in the Netherlands

The Netherlands has more inland waterways per square kilometre than any other country in the world. It is one of the few countries where the length of the waterway network exceeds that of the railways. There are 4380 km of Dutch inland waterways and they carry one-third of the total freight carried in the country.

The waterways can be divided into three types: rivers, canals and ship canals. Only one-fifth of the waterways are made up of rivers. The Rijn, Lek, Waal and Maas are all navigable for barges of over 2000 tonnes. As Figure E shows, large canals link every region of the Netherlands. All the major canals have been upgraded to take barges of 1350 tonnes, declared the standard barge size by the EC. Three very large and deep ship canals have been built to allow large ocean-going ships to enter the ports of Rotterdam (the New Waterway), Amsterdam (the North Sea Canal) and Ghent (the Ghent–Terneuzen Canal).

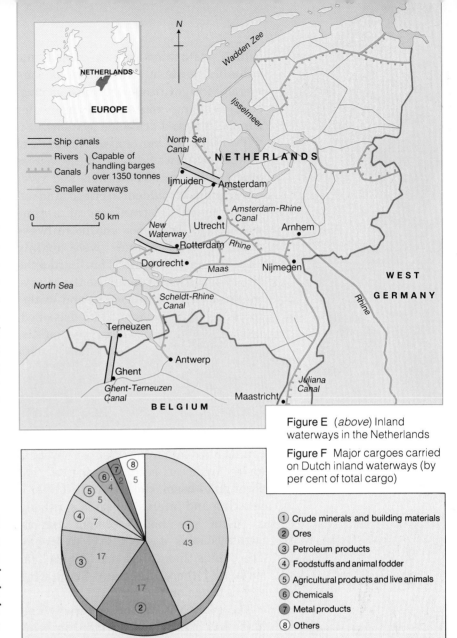

Figure E (*above*) Inland waterways in the Netherlands

Figure F Major cargoes carried on Dutch inland waterways (by per cent of total cargo)

① Crude minerals and building materials
② Ores
③ Petroleum products
④ Foodstuffs and animal fodder
⑤ Agricultural products and live animals
⑥ Chemicals
⑦ Metal products
⑧ Others

QUESTIONS

1 a) What is a 'push-tow barge train'?
   b) Make a sketch of the barge train in Figure A and say what advantages barge trains have over single barges.

2 In which four European countries is inland waterway transport most important?

3 What are the advantages of inland waterway transport compared with road or rail?

4 a) What is the standard European barge size declared by the EC?
   b) Why do you think a standard barge size was introduced?

5 Figure F shows the major cargoes carried on Dutch inland waterways.
   a) Name the three most important cargoes.
   b) Why is inland waterway transport especially suited to carrying these three cargoes?

4.7 Inland waterways in Britain

Inland waterways are a varied and valuable resource. They serve as commercial freight transport links, as pleasure cruising routes and as water supply and land drainage systems.

Two hundred years ago a network of inland waterways was built across much of Britain. The canals and river navigations provided a cheap and efficient means of transport at a time when roads were poor and no railways existed. British canals were mainly built to a narrow width. This limited the size of barge which could use the canals. In many parts of Europe inland waterways have been widened and deepened. In Britain this rarely happened and the canals were unable to compete with improved road and rail transport.

Today, little freight is transported on the narrow canals. Only the broader canals and rivers remain important for freight (Figure C). Many of the narrow canals have fallen into disuse. Yet some have found a second lease of life through tourism. Holidays afloat offer a relaxing and interesting time. Cruising at 6 km per hour through remote countryside is a great way to travel. The canals themselves are historic features and there are many fascinating sights to see on the way.

The growth in inland waterway holidays has created employment in boatyards building and servicing vessels. It has brought life back to canalside shops

Figure A (*right*) Scenes from today's inland waterways: coal barges on the Aire and Calder Navigation (*top*), a ship on the Gloucester and Sharpness Ship Canal (*middle*), and a derelict canal (*bottom*)

and pubs which declined as the commercial traffic died. The success of canal holidays has led to the reopening of several derelict sections of canal such as the Stratford-upon-Avon Canal and the Kennet and Avon Navigation.

In some parts of the country freight transport by inland waterway remains important. Over 60 million tonnes of cargo a year is carried. There is a growing trade on several rivers, notably the Trent. New wharves have been built at Gainsborough and at Keadby to take cargo ships of up to 2500 tonnes. The British Waterways Board, which operates much of Britain's inland waterway system, is at present enlarging its commercial waterways from 700 to 1500 tonnes capacity.

Figure B A narrow boat, specially designed to navigate Britain's narrow canals, now used for tourism

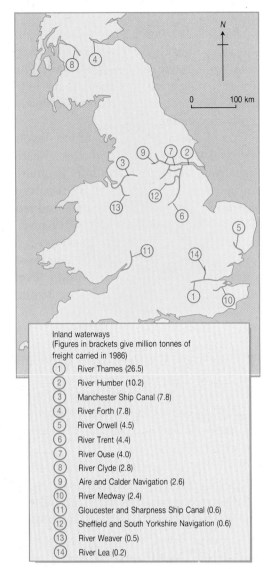

Inland waterways
(Figures in brackets give million tonnes of
freight carried in 1986)

①	River Thames (26.5)
②	River Humber (10.2)
③	Manchester Ship Canal (7.8)
④	River Forth (7.8)
⑤	River Orwell (4.5)
⑥	River Trent (4.4)
⑦	River Ouse (4.0)
⑧	River Clyde (2.8)
⑨	Aire and Calder Navigation (2.6)
⑩	River Medway (2.4)
⑪	Gloucester and Sharpness Ship Canal (0.6)
⑫	Sheffield and South Yorkshire Navigation (0.6)
⑬	River Weaver (0.5)
⑭	River Lea (0.2)

Figure C Britain's inland waterways

The Severn Corridor

Worcester, 100 km from the open sea, was once an important river port. Barges of up to 400 tonnes sailed up the River Severn to the city's small dock basin. By the 1960s freight traffic on the Severn beyond Tewkesbury had ended. Cargo vessels still use the Severn Corridor. The Gloucester and Sharpness Ship Canal allows coasters of 750 tonnes to travel as far inland as Gloucester.

The British Waterways Board plans to improve the Ship Canal so that ocean-going ships of 2500 tonnes can reach Gloucester. At a later stage the River Severn would be improved between Gloucester and Worcester. Bridges would be raised and widened, locks enlarged and river banks strengthened. Low-profile sea-going ships of 1500 tonnes could reach the improved docks at Worcester. It is hoped that Worcester would become a major inland freight centre, channelling the trade to and from the West Midlands and Ireland, France, Spain and the east coast of North America.

A revival of inland waterway transport would be to Britain's economic advantage. Modern waterways provide cheap and efficient transport for bulk and containerized cargo. Canal transport does much less damage to the environment than the heavy lorries on which Britain's transport system is firmly based. Canal transport is also a more efficient user of energy, less noisy and safer.

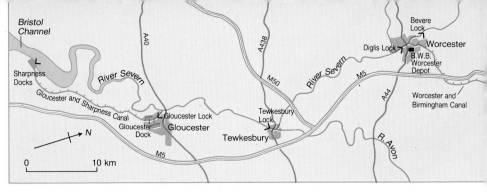

Figure D The Severn Corridor

QUESTIONS

1 List the uses of inland waterways in Britain.

2 What are the attractions of an inland waterway holiday?

3 What advantages has tourism provided for Britain's inland waterways?

4 Study Figure C.
a) Draw a bar graph to illustrate the statistics in the table.
b) What is the annual total of freight carried on all Britain's inland waterways?
c) What are the advantages of inland waterways as a means of freight transport?
d) Can you think of any disadvantages of inland waterways for freight transport?

5 a) Copy the map of the Severn Corridor (Figure D).
b) Name the towns shown by their first letters, using an atlas to help you.
c) What is the approximate length of (i) the Gloucester and Sharpness Canal (ii) the River Severn from Gloucester to Worcester?
d) What are the advantages of Worcester as the site for an inland freight centre?
e) What developments are planned for the Severn Corridor?

Water is the essence of life. Access to pure water is vital for the survival of human beings. Many deadly diseases such as cholera and typhoid are spread by unclean water. Throughout the world millions of people die each year because of dirty water.

It is in all our interests to secure and preserve pure water supplies. Yet many human activities are having the opposite effect: polluting water supplies.

Water pollution can be measured by the amount of dissolved oxygen present. Clean water has a reading of 100 per cent. Under normal conditions water will purify itself. Waste materials including dead fish and plants will be broken-down by the oxygen and bacteria in the water. Plants release fresh oxygen into the water and maintain the dissolved oxygen balance. The water's *ecosystem* is in a state of harmony.

If water has a low dissolved oxygen reading it shows that oxygen is being used up by bacteria in the water faster than it dissolves into the stream from the air or from the oxygenating plants. Fish die without dissolved oxygen. Green plants called algae grow on the surface of the water. They prevent light passing through. The oxygenating plants die because of lack of light. The water turns cloudy and dark. It starts to smell. The ecosystem has broken-down; the water is dead.

One of the major causes of low levels of dissolved oxygen is pollution. Readings from the River Trent in England showed a 96 per cent level of dissolved oxygen in the river north of the industrial city of Stoke-on-Trent. After passing through Stoke the dissolved oxygen level fell to just 21 per cent. The river did not regain the previous high level until it had flowed on for another 35 km.

The main human pollutants are:

1 Sewage which contains bacteria that can spread disease, plus nutrients which encourage the growth of algae. In Britain there has been much investment in sewage treatment (Figure B) and sewage is no longer the major pollutant it once was.

2 Industrial waste includes a wide range of poisonous chemicals such as cyanide, arsenic, mercury and lead. These can destroy all life in the water.

Figure A A polluted stream

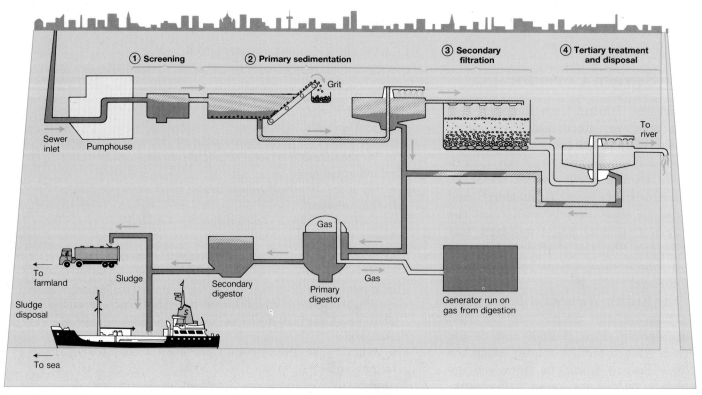

Figure B The sewage treatment process

Figure C A sewage works

Mercury and lead can kill human brain cells and produce deformities in unborn children.

3 Thermal pollution, or more simply, hot water. Power stations use water for cooling and return it to a river at a higher temperature. This can be disastrous. Warm water can hold less oxygen than cool water. At 31°C fish die. At 38°C typhus bacteria grow.

4 Agricultural waste has increased rapidly recently. Slurry from livestock may equal the amount of sewage disposed of by a small town. Leaks from silage are 200 times more polluting than sewage. Fertilizers and pesticides are regularly washed from the fields into rivers by rainwater. They add nitrates, phosphates, zinc and mercury to the water, poisoning the fish and plants. Humans are also at risk: drinking water containing nitrates can kill young children.

Most pollution could be stopped. However, pollution control is expensive and many polluters will not pay the price unless forced to do so. Anti-pollution laws have been introduced by the government, but in 1987 the Department of the Environment stated that pollution in Britain's rivers increased for the first time since the 1950s. Clearly, further efforts are needed to provide clean water.

QUESTIONS

1 Why is it vital to have supplies of clean water?

2 How are waste materials normally broken-down in a river?

3 What can you tell about the conditions in a river if the following levels of dissolved oxygen are found: (a) 100 per cent, and (b) 20 per cent?

4 a) How does sewage pollution affect a river?
b) Draw a flow diagram to show the main stages of sewage treatment, based on Figure B.

5 a) What is thermal water pollution?
b) How does thermal pollution affect a river?

6 a) Why has the pollution of water by agricultural wastes increased rapidly recently?
b) What effects may agricultural pollution have?

7 Fieldwork project
You can carry out your own survey of water pollution. This is what you can do:
a) Choose a section of a stream which seems to be polluted (most streams in towns will be!). You should study at least 3 km of stream channel.
b) *Be careful*! Any stream can be dangerous, and polluted streams may be a health hazard. Do not drink the water. Be sure to wash carefully when you return home. It is sensible to wear rubber boots and rubber gloves.
c) Equipment. You will need: (i) a clipboard (ii) a thermometer (iii) pH litmus papers (iv) sample bottles.
d) Walk along your section of stream and make a simple map. Show on your map any possible sources of pollution such as factory or sewage outfalls.
e) Select ten sites along the river to carry out sample studies.
f) At each of your ten sites record the evidence for pollution using a table like this:

Stream Pollution Survey			
NAME			
Stream name		Sample site no.	
OS grid reference		Date	
Water temperature °C		pH	
Colour		Clarity	
Algae		Smell	
Litter			

g) Measure the water temperature using the thermometer.
h) Measure the pH of the water using the litmus paper. An unpolluted stream will have a pH of between 5.5 and 7.0. A pH above 7.0 indicates alkali pollution; a pH below 5.5 indicates acid pollution.
i) Take a sample of the water in a bottle and smell it. Record any unpleasant smelling samples. Record the colour of the water and compare it with the other samples.

4.9
Water
pollution

The River Rhine has long had an evil reputation. It has been called 'Europe's Sewer'. The homes and factories of six nations pour their waste into the river.

Figure A The River Rhine and its tributaries

NETHERLANDS

Rotterdam
Oil refining
Chemicals

Ruhr
industrial area
Coal
Steel
Chemicals
Oil refining
Engineering

Ruhr

WEST GERMANY

BELGIUM

Meuse

Rhine

Rhine-Main
industrial area
Oil refining
Chemicals
Plastics
Engineering

LUXEMBOURG

Main

Saar
Coal

Neckar

Lorraine
Chemicals
Iron, steel

Stuttgart
Textiles
Cars

FRANCE

Moselle

Strasbourg
Chemicals
Oil refining

N

Alsace
Potash
Chemicals

Rhine

0   100 km

Basle
Chemicals

LIECHTENSTEIN   AUSTRIA

SWITZERLAND

Figure B The BASF chemical plant at Ludwigshafen

By the time the Rhine enters the Netherlands it is heavily polluted. Yet over half of the Dutch drinking-water has to be extracted from the river.

Chemical pollution is especially serious. Most of the chemicals can be broken-down and dispersed naturally by bacteria, but this takes time and reduces the amount of oxygen dissolved in the water. Without oxygen, there can be no fish or plant life; the river dies.

Some of the world's largest chemical factories are located beside the River Rhine. They are attracted by the cooling water and the oil pipelines which follow the Rhine Valley, plus the vast market for chemicals in the countries through which the Rhine flows. They pump their waste into the river. Concentrations of salt, chloride and hydrochloric acid in the Rhine are sometimes up to four times the natural average.

In 1986 . . . . . water from farms.

BASF Ludwigshafen

The largest of the Rhineside chemical factories is sited at Ludwigshafen. This vast complex stretches 5 km along the Rhine. It is owned by BASF. There are 1800 separate plants with over 50 000 workers. In 1986 the complex produced 7.8 million tonnes of chemicals, including video tape, recording tape, plastics, fertilizers and medicines. The works produces several million tonnes of waste each year.

BASF has its own pollution control centre. They spend £500 million a year on controlling their effluent. A giant plant has been built to clean waste water before it is dumped into the Rhine. As well as dealing with BASF's effluent, the plant also processes the sewage from the towns of Ludwigshafen and Frankenthal. It removes impurities from some 600 000 cubic metres of water per day! The water which is returned to the Rhine is estimated to be 95 per cent clean. The plant opened in 1974. Unfortunately, there have been problems. The plant produces un-

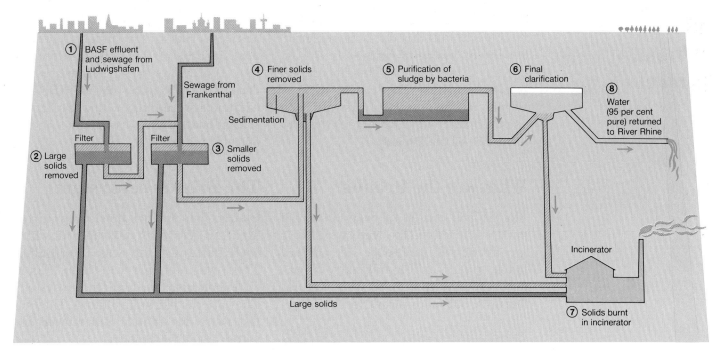

Within the figure:

① BASF effluent and sewage from Ludwigshafen

Sewage from Frankenthal

④ Finer solids removed

⑤ Purification of sludge by bacteria

⑥ Final clarification

⑧ Water (95 per cent pure) returned to River Rhine

Filter

Filter

Sedimentation

② Large solids removed

③ Smaller solids removed

Incinerator

Large solids

⑦ Solids burnt in incinerator

Figure C The pollution control process at BASF Ludwigshafen

pleasant smells which lead to regular complaints from nearby residents. BASF has finally agreed to cover much of the plant with plastic and install pumps to aerate the water by driving oxygen through it.

BASF's measures have improved the quality of the Rhine. They also save the company money. The incinerators which burn waste also provide more than half of the steam used at Ludwigshafen, greatly cutting the company's energy bill. Savings are also made through reclaiming some of the valuable chemicals once disposed of in the plant's effluent.

Other projects to help protect the Rhine have been undertaken by BASF. These include new monitoring stations to analyse emissions in the river and a research laboratory to study the effects of emissions upon fish. By 1976 fish were returning to the once heavily polluted Ludwigshafen section of the Rhine.

In 1986 most of the fish died. They were killed by a leak of mercury and other poisons into the Rhine at Basle in Switzerland. A warehouse owned by Sandoz, a chemical company, caught fire. The pollution was clearly followed in a trail of dead fish from Basle to the North Sea, affecting France, West Germany and the Netherlands. This was a disaster, but within a year the Rhine had recovered – a sure testimony to the efforts of companies such as BASF to 'clean up their act' and cut their effluent. The Rhine is now cleaner than it has been for many decades. However, much remains to be done before the Rhine loses its evil reputation.

QUESTIONS

1 Study Figure A.
   a) Where is the source of the River Rhine?
   b) Name the six countries through which the Rhine and its tributaries flow.
   c) Name four of the major industrial areas sited along the Rhine or its tributaries and name their main industries.

2 What are the effects of chemical pollution on a river?

3 a) What event in 1986 showed the deadly effects of chemical pollution on the River Rhine?
   b) Describe what happened and its results.

4 a) Describe the BASF chemical works at Ludwigshafen.
   b) Name five products of the BASF works.

5 a) How does the BASF plant process its waste?
   b) What benefits are there for BASF in processing its waste?
   c) What problem was created by the BASF pollution control plant?
   d) What other environmental measures have been taken by BASF?

Figure A shows a typical summer scene in the Norfolk Broads. This region of waterways is one of Britain's most important holiday areas. This apparently peaceful area is actually the scene of serious conflict between different land uses, a conflict which threatens the very existence of the Broads.

What are the Broads?

The Broads consist of over 200 km of partly tidal navigable waterways. It is an attractive landscape of shallow lakes, rivers and marshland. It was once thought that they were natural features, but more recent research sug-gests that they are the result of human activity. During the Middle Ages the peat deposits of the area were dug for fuel. Vast pits were formed which became waterlogged to form the Broads. Channels were dug to link the Broads so that boats could carry produce in and out of the area.

The Broads ecosystem

Plants, fish and wildfowl grew in the area. An *ecosystem* developed in which each natural thing was inter-linked. There was a simple food chain (Figure C). People also fitted into the ecosystem. They ate the fish and wildfowl. They cut the reeds for thatch and mowed the water meadows for hay.

The threat to the Broads

Since the 1940s the Broads have been under threat. The water and waterside plants have declined rapidly. Even the vast reed-beds have been disappearing. The numbers of fish and wildfowl have fallen. Several of the Broads have shrunk in size.

The threat to the Broads comes from several sources:

1 Tourism. Early tourists sailed yachts or caught fish. They had little effect upon the Broads. More recently motorboats have become the main type of craft using the Broads. The wash from the motorboats erodes the river banks and stirs up the mud. The Broads have become very congested during the summer. In addition to boating holidays there are also many caravan sites and holiday bungalows. Tourism earns over £15 million per year in the Broads and provides many jobs.

2 Sewage. Twenty outlets discharge partly treated sewage into the Broads. It would be very expensive to purify the sewage.

3 Farming. In the past much of the marshland separating the Broads has been reclaimed for pasture. Recently the meadows have been converted into

Figure A

Figure B The Norfolk Broads

arable fields growing mainly cereals. The farmers were encouraged to do this by government grants. Nitrate and phosphate fertilizers are used on the fields. They are washed by rainwater into the Broads to cause serious pollution. Algae grow in the polluted water, reducing the oxygen content, and killing the plants and animals.

Action has been taken. For many years farmers demanded that water levels in the Broads should be lowered so that they could drain more fields. The battle ended only when the farmers were paid £123 per hectare to keep the land available for grazing. The money is provided by the Countryside Commission and the Ministry of Agriculture, Forestry and Fisheries. This has been done under the European Community's 'Environmentally Sensitive Areas' policy established in 1985.

The unique landscape and atmosphere of the Broads has been damaged by farming and tourism. The congestion and pollution has discouraged many tourists. Since 1976 over 400 hire motorboats have been withdrawn and several boatyards and hire companies have gone out of business.

Controlling the Broads

In 1947 it was proposed that the Broads should become a National Park. This did not happen. For thirty years the responsibility for running the Broads was split between several different organizations and councils. No one had overall control. Then in 1978 the Broads Authority was established. It was a committee of local councils which dealt with planning and leisure but had no powers to control the waterways.

Finally, in 1986, the government announced that the Norfolk Broads were to be given the status of a National Park with a single controlling authority. At last the conflicts threatening the Broads may be solved and this unique landscape may be preserved for future generations.

Figure C The Norfolk Broads ecosystem, and a simple food chain

Herons
Hawks
Wildfowl
Food chain
Insects
Reeds
Water insects
Fish

QUESTIONS

1 a) What are the Norfolk Broads?
b) How were the Broads formed?

2 a) Draw a simple flow diagram to show the food chain which developed in the Norfolk Broads.
b) How did people traditionally fit into the ecosystem?

3 What problems face the Broads?

4 How do the following threaten the Broads: (a) tourism (b) sewage (c) farming?

5 Study the table below:

Number of motorboats on the Norfolk Broads

Year	1950	1955	1960	1965	1970	1975	1980	1985
Number of boats	3100	3450	4000	4550	5150	5850	6100	5700

a) Draw a line graph to illustrate these statistics.
b) Why has the number of motorboats fallen since 1980?

6 What are the advantages of a National Park Authority for the Norfolk Broads?

Unit 4 ASSESSMENT

1 Study Figure A and answer the following questions.
 a) In which mountain range does the Sacramento River have its source? (1 mark)
 b) In which compass direction does the Sacramento flow, downstream of the Shasta Dam? (1 mark)
 c) The southern Central Valley is irrigated by water transfer schemes. What do you understand by (i) irrigation and (ii) water transfer? (4 marks)
 d) How much land is irrigated within the Central Valley? (1 mark)
 e) Why is it necessary for the southern Central Valley to be irrigated? (2 marks)
 f) What problems have been created by the Central Valley project? (4 marks)
 g) Name another example of a large-scale water transfer scheme for the purpose of irrigation. (1 mark)
 h) With the aid of a sketch map, describe the major features of your named water transfer scheme. (10 marks)

2 a) Name an example of a large reservoir which met opposition during its construction. (1 mark)
 b) State the arguments of two groups of people who did not wish to see the reservoir completed. (4 marks)

3 Study Figure B and answer the following questions.
 a) Name the type of rock labelled A on the diagram. (1 mark)
 b) Is this rock permeable or impermeable? (1 mark)
 c) What is an aquifer? (2 marks)
 d) Name two types of rock (other than the type you have named above) which are aquifers. (2 marks)
 e) What does the line labelled B on the diagram represent? (1 mark)
 f) (i) What feature would you expect to find at C on the diagram? (1 mark)
  (ii) Explain why you would expect to find such a feature there. (2 marks)

Figure A

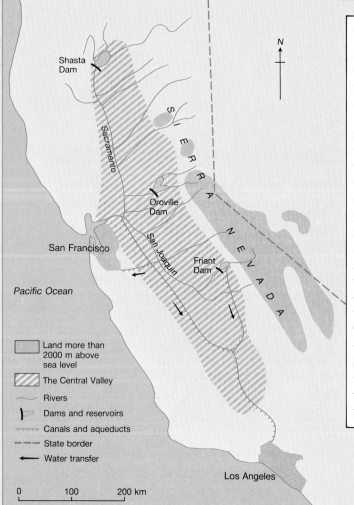

Land more than 2000 m above sea level
The Central Valley
Rivers
Dams and reservoirs
Canals and aqueducts
State border
Water transfer

0   100   200 km

The Central Valley Project

Most of California's water supply is in the less developed, less populated area of northern California. Over five-eighths of the demand is in the central and southern areas where rainfall is below 400 mm per year. The Central Valley of California is the largest area of irrigated land in North America. It is supplied with water mainly from the Sacramento River which starts in the snowfields of the Sierra Nevada mountains.

The Sacramento River has been dammed to conserve water. Canals and aqueducts carry the water over 200 km from the Sacramento to the dry lands of the southern Central Valley. Over 2 million hectares of land are irrigated within the Central Valley. The California Aqueduct carries Sacramento water even further southwards to the Los Angeles area. Much water is also diverted to meet the domestic and industrial demands of the rapidly growing Californian towns.

There have been problems. The high temperatures cause the build up of salt in the soil which reduces crop yields. Subsidence has been caused by water extraction. The reservoirs are silting up. Farmers have to pay high water charges which put up the cost of produce and reduce farm wages.

Figure B The London Basin

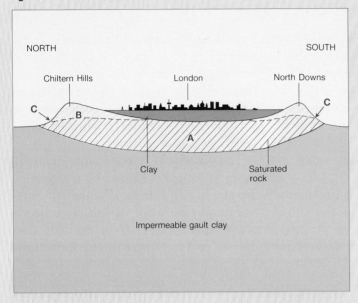

4 a) What are the advantages of inland waterways as a
means of freight transport? (4 marks)
b) Name four major inland waterways used for freight
transport in Europe. (2 marks)
c) What is a barge train? (1 mark)
d) What are the advantages of a barge train? (2 marks)
e) How can inland waterways be used for tourism?
(2 marks)

Figure C

5 a) Name a river or lake in the British Isles where the
purity of water has been destroyed by human action.
(1 mark)

b) Explain fully three ways in which pollution has
occurred there. (9 marks)

TOTAL: 60 marks

Details for pupil profile sheet Unit 4

Knowledge and understanding

1 Hydrological cycle
2 Over-exploitation of water resources
3 Geographical imbalance of water supplies in Great Britain
4 Aquifer; spring; spa
5 Multi-purpose water project
6 Watershed
7 Importance of inland waterway transport in Western Europe
8 Leisure and freight opportunities on British inland waterways
9 Effects of water pollution
10 Ecosystem

Skills

1 Completing a systems diagram
2 Draw a divided bar
3 Designing a publicity pamphlet
4 Draw a bar graph
5 Recording a news report on tape or video
6 Naming towns on a map with the aid of an atlas
7 Fieldwork survey of water pollution
8 Draw a line graph
9 Draw a flow diagram
10 Draw a sketch map

Values

1 Benefits and costs of a major water engineering project
2 Conflicts over land use in recreational areas

Unit 5: Primary products from the developing world

Figure A shows the crowded port of Dar es Salaam in Tanzania. One of the ships in the background is loading coffee for export. When the ship's hold is full, it will sail 14 000 km to the port of Bristol in England. Such voyages are vital to Tanzania. Over half of Tanzania's export earnings come from sales of coffee.

Tanzania has little manufacturing industry. Nine out of ten of the ships leaving Dar es Salaam carry primary products: sisal, cotton and diamonds, but mainly coffee. Tanzania's coffee exports have to pay for the manufactured goods which the country has to import. Ships arriving at Dar es Salaam unload such important goods as tractors, lorries, chemicals, plastics, steel, fertilizer and medicines.

Tanzania's over-dependence upon primary products is shared by many other developing countries (Figure B). Some are at the mercy of variations in world commodity prices. If prices fall they cannot pay to import the manufactured

Figure A

goods which they need, or to build the clinics, schools and other vital services needed by their people.

How has this over-dependence upon primary products come about? It is largely the result of the colonial period. The colonial countries developed manufacturing industries which needed raw materials. The people of Tanzania used to grow millet as their main food crop. The German colonizers took control of the best land by force. They made the Tanzanians grow sisal, coffee and cotton instead of food. Railways and roads were built to the main cash crop producing areas to rush the commodities to the ports of Dar es Salaam and Tanga. The commodities were taken to Germany where they were used to produce manufactured goods in German factories.

The export corridors established by the Germans remain in use today. Tanzania's transport system remains dominated by the need to supply commodities to the developed world. There is little trade between Tanzania and its neighbouring countries, apart from Kenya. The colonial trade system survives almost intact. The developed countries continue to benefit at the expense of the developing countries.

Three hundred years ago, India was one of the world's most highly developed nations. The Indian textile industry produced some of the world's best cloth: muslin, velvet, silk and, most important of all, cotton. During the eighteenth century, Great Britain invaded India and took control by force. The British destroyed the Indian textile industry by taxing exports of Indian cloth and buying raw cotton. Cotton cloth was sent back to India. India's industrial exports (textiles) had been replaced by the export of a primary commodity (cotton). Since independence from Britain in 1947 India has struggled to rebuild its industrial economy and escape from the colonial system.

Figure B Primary commodities exported from selected countries

Country	Primary commodities as a percentage of total exports	Major commodities exported	GDP per person ($)
Burundi	100	Coffee, tea, cotton	238
Libya	100	Crude oil	9050
Rwanda	100	Coffee, tea, tin	250
Cuba	99	Sugar, tobacco	1425
Iraq	99	Crude oil, dates	3700
Mali	99	Cotton, peanuts	295
Somalia	99	Live animals, bananas	305
Uganda	99	Coffe, cotton, copper	220
Ecuador	98	Bananas, coffee, crude oil	1450
Gabon	98	Crude oil, timber	3250

Figure C Tanzania's trade

Exports		Imports	
Commodity	Percentage of total export earnings	Commodity	Percentage of total import costs
Coffee	54	Machinery	27
Cotton	17	Vehicles	8
Sisal	7	Textiles	11
Diamonds	5	Petroleum products	30
Cashew nuts	4	Iron and steel	6
Others	13	Others	18
Total: $370 million	**100**	**Total: $830 million**	**100**

QUESTIONS

1 Study Figure C.
   a) Draw two divided bars to represent the trade of Tanzania.
   b) What differences are there between Tanzania's exports and imports?
   c) What are the causes of these differences?
   d) Tanzania has a 'balance of trade deficit' of $460 million. What does this mean?
   e) What other sources of income might the government of Tanzania have to help pay for the imports?

2 Why are exports of primary commodities vital to many developing countries?

3 Study Figure B.
   a) What problems do the countries in the table face because of their over-dependence upon primary commodities?
   b) Name the three countries with the highest GDP per person.
   c) Suggest why these countries are much richer than the others in the table.

4 Many developing countries are over-dependent upon primary commodities. How has this happened?

Study Figure A and **answer questions 1 and 2** before carrying on reading.

Figure A Nigeria's exports (by value), 1967, 1980 and 1986

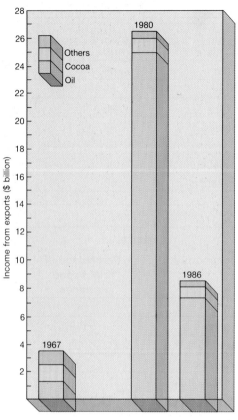

Figure B Nigeria

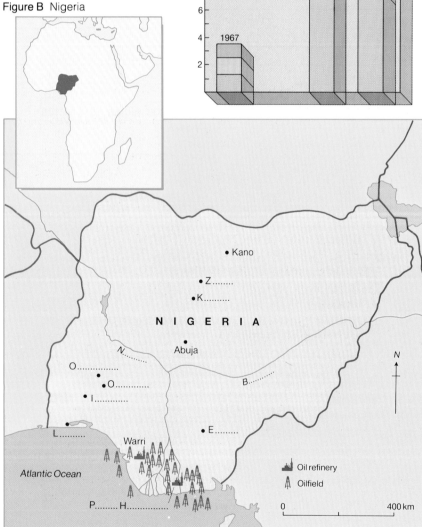

Oil was first produced in Nigeria during the 1950s. There are now over 60 oilfields producing 70 million tonnes of oil per year. Most of Nigeria's oil is exported to the USA and Europe from deepwater terminals built offshore or from the port facilities at Port Harcourt.

Slowly at first, but with increasing pace, oil came to dominate Nigeria's economy:

● up to 98 per cent of Nigeria's export earnings came from oil

● up to 85 per cent of the government's total revenue came from oil

● agriculture was badly hit: output of cash crops such as cocoa has fallen

● living standards rose, especially in the cities

● people moved in great numbers to the cities

● imported consumer goods flooded into Nigeria

The 1970s were boom years for Nigeria. Money from oil exports poured into the country. Much of the money was spent on developing manufacturing industry, the intention being to replace imports by home production and provide jobs. Oil refineries, petro-chemicals, paper, cement, textiles and vehicle assembly factories were amongst the new industries. Other major developments included roads, armaments and a scheme to build a new capital city at Abuja. The great expense of these developments was only partly met by oil revenues. Much of the cost was met by loans from banks in the developed world. By 1980 Nigeria had fallen £20 billion into debt!

The loans were to be paid back using future oil earnings. Unfortunately, the fall in oil prices was devastating for Nigeria. Between 1980 and 1986 the country's oil earnings fell from over $26 billion to only $8.5 billion. Nigeria's other exports had declined and could not fill the gap in income. The Nigerian government cut back on spending, raised food prices and cut oil

Figure C An oil well in the Nigerian countryside

Figure D A busy street scene in Lagos

prices. This resulted in unrest, followed by a successful military coup in 1984 which overthrew the civilian government.

The collapse of Nigeria's oil earnings has caused a rapid decline in the people's standard of living. This has caused a sharp fall in demand for manufactured goods. Nigeria's new industries have faltered: for example, four of Nigeria's seven vehicle assembly plants closed during 1986.

Nigeria's ambitious plans have been destroyed by the fall in oil prices. The government is now trying to lead the economy away from its crippling over-dependence upon oil. A new emphasis is being placed upon agriculture. Imports of rice and wheat have been banned, giving a boost to local food crops. At the same time the value of Nigeria's cocoa and groundnut exports has more than doubled between 1986 and 1987.

QUESTIONS

1 Study Figure A.
a) What were the total export earnings of Nigeria in
(i) 1967 (ii) 1980 (iii) 1986?
b) What percentage of Nigeria's total exports consisted of oil in
(i) 1967 (ii) 1980 (iii) 1986?

2 a) In which year was Nigeria's export trade most diverse?
b) What happened to Nigeria's export trade (i) between 1967 and 1980 (ii) between 1980 and 1986?
c) What appears to be the main cause of the fall in export earnings between 1980 and 1987?

3 a) Copy the map of Nigeria (Figure B).
b) Using your atlas to help you, name:
(i) the countries surrounding Nigeria
(ii) the towns shown by their first letters
(iii) the rivers.

4 a) Where are Nigeria's oilfields located?
b) How much oil does Nigeria produce per year?

5 a) What evidence is there that oil came to dominate Nigeria's economy?
b) What problems did this create for Nigeria?

6 Study the people shown in Figure D.
a) Where do these people live?
b) How may their lives have been affected by Nigeria's reliance upon oil?

6 You are a member of the government of Nigeria. Prepare a plan to lead the Nigerian economy away from its over-dependence upon oil. What should the oil revenues be spent on?

A North-South pattern of trade developed during the nineteenth century. It was based on the colonial system. The developed countries extracted the resources from the colonies and sold manufactured goods back to them. This unjust system has continued despite the break-up of the colonial empires during the twentieth century. Japan has emerged as a new industrial power. It has forged trade links with Asia and Australasia which are similar to those established by Europe and North America.

This simple pattern creates a difficult problem. Prices of resources are low compared with the prices of manufactured goods, and the gap is steadily increasing. For example, in 1960 two tonnes of tea bought a tractor; by 1988 20 tonnes of tea were needed!

Figure A These two diagrams illustrate the pattern of world trade in very simplified terms

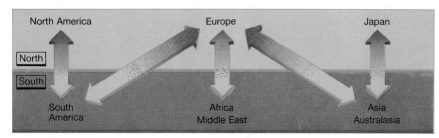

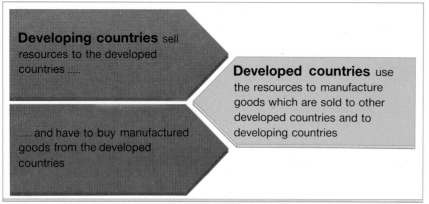

Figure C The amount of rubber needed to buy one tractor

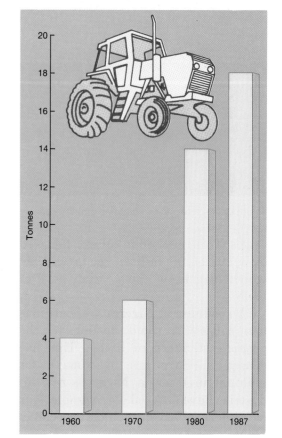

Figure B West African timber unloaded on the West Wharf quay at Avonmouth, Bristol

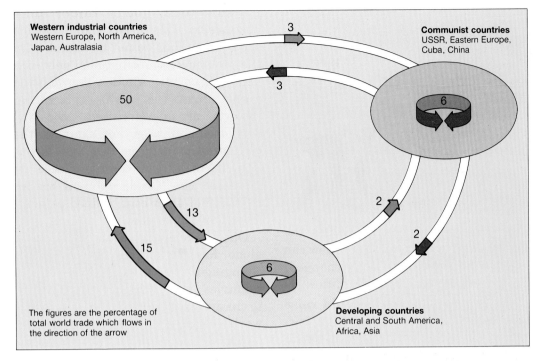

Western industrial countries
Western Europe, North America, Japan, Australasia

Communist countries
USSR, Eastern Europe, Cuba, China

Developing countries
Central and South America, Africa, Asia

The figures are the percentage of total world trade which flows in the direction of the arrow

Figure D The proportions of world trade

Prices of manufactured goods have increased steadily. Prices of resources have gone up and down depending upon demand. Developing countries often depend upon the export of only a very few resources. If resource prices fall, such developing countries are in serious trouble. They can only afford to progress by borrowing money from the rich nations.

What makes the resource prices vary so much? Prices may fall because of changes in demand. For example, aluminium has replaced copper for some purposes such as electrical connections. Supply and demand affect prices. Harvests of agricultural resources may be affected by drought or disease. This makes the resource scarce and the price rises. A glut will lead to a fall in prices.

Prices for many resources are fixed by the consuming nations in the developed world. They have the money to buy most of the resources. By contrast, the developing countries cannot afford the manufactured goods they need to import.

QUESTIONS

1 What is the general pattern of world trade?

2 Study Figure D. What percentage of world trade consists of:
   a) Trade between the Western industrial nations?
   b) Trade between the communist nations?
   c) Trade between the developing countries?
   d) Trade between the developing countries and (i) the West (ii) the communist nations?
   e) How did this pattern of trade develop?

3 What problems are created by the pattern of world trade?

4 Study Figure C.
   a) How many tonnes of rubber were needed to buy one tractor in 1960?
   b) How many tonnes were needed to buy one tractor in 1987?
   c) What has happened to the prices of rubber and tractors between 1960 and 1987?

5 Study Figure E.
   a) What was the price of Malaysian tin in 1976?
   b) How has the price changed sinced 1976?
   c) Why do prices of resources such as tin vary so much?

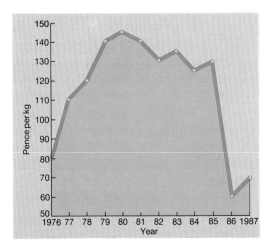

Figure E The price of Malaysian tin, 1976–87

5.4 Breaking the chains

Figure A (*from top right to bottom*) The cover of the Brandt Report, jars of coffee, OPEC Ministers, and an oil rig

Figure B Members of OPEC

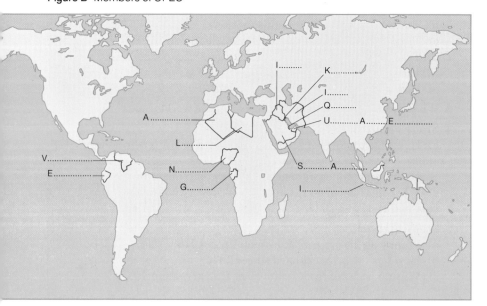

On the previous pages we studied the present pattern of world trade. How can this unfair pattern of trade be changed? There are a number of possibilities:

1. Developing countries could raise the price of their resources. However, attempts to do this have met with varied success. In 1980 the Ivory Coast stored its cocoa rather than sell it. It was an attempt to create a shortage of cocoa and so raise prices. Other developing countries simply increased their production to replace the lost cocoa. In any case, cocoa is not an essential product. If the price had risen a lot, people would have bought less.

2. Developed countries could charge less for their manufactured goods. This is unlikely unless there is some clear advantage to be gained.

3. Developing countries could build up their own industries and sell manufactured goods rather than resources. This needs money which the poor nations do not have and, with the problems of international debt, can no longer borrow. Another reason is the higher taxes, or tariffs, placed on imports of manufactured goods by developed countries. For example, the EC places no tariffs on rice imports, but a tariff of 13 per cent is placed on processed rice. Crude palm-oil has an EC tariff of 4 per cent, refined palm-oil a tariff of 12 per cent.

One developing country working alone has little hope of success in changing the terms of trade. Only when countries group together can they hope to change the situation. The developing world's major oil producing nations formed a group called OPEC (Organization of Petroleum Exporting Countries). The group's aim was to obtain a higher price for oil, which was very cheap at the time.

By 1973 OPEC produced 90 per cent of all the oil in world trade. OPEC was in a powerful position. Unlike cocoa, oil is an essential resource. In 1973 OPEC raised the price of oil from $3 to $12 a barrel. Money poured into the OPEC countries. This created economic problems for developed countries. Even more serious was the effect upon the oil importing developing countries – the oil price rise brought disaster to their fragile economies.

Another round of oil price rises in 1979 helped plunge the world into deep economic recession. The industries of the developed countries declined. This led to a fall in demand for resources and a fall in prices. The developed countries raised the price of their manufactured goods in order to pay for the more expensive oil. The oil importing developing countries suffered in every way: much higher prices for their essential imports, oil and manufactured goods, plus lower prices for their resources.

The pattern of world trade is unfair. It is also short-sighted. If the developing countries remain poor they will be unable to afford to buy manufactured goods from the developed countries. Jobs will be lost and the economies of developed countries will suffer. It is clear that a complete adjustment of world trade is needed with increased and stable prices for resources. The Brandt Report of 1980, produced by a group of leading politicians and economists from all over the world, urged change.

The Brandt Commission published a second report in 1983 entitled 'Common Crisis: Co-operation for World Recovery' which stressed that progress must be made in changing the terms of trade – for the benefit of all. Such progress can only be made if both developing and developed countries work together. OPEC was unable to prevent a sharp fall in oil prices during the 1980s because its share of world oil trade had fallen. Developed countries which exported oil, such as the UK and Norway, refused to join OPEC and sold oil more cheaply than OPEC countries. There has been more progress towards co-operation between developed and developing countries with a number of international commodity agreements such as those of the International Coffee Organization. The ICO sets quotas for producing nations in order to keep coffee prices stable. Tough negotiations are needed to achieve a price which everyone agrees on.

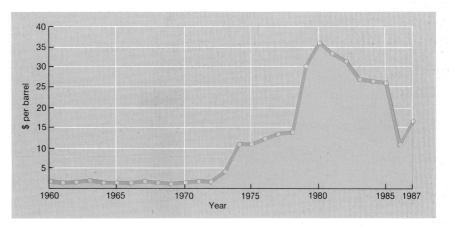

Figure C World oil prices, 1960–87

Countertrade

One way for developing countries to overcome their lack of money is to set up 'countertrade' agreements. This means that a country pays for imported goods not with money but with goods. This is becoming increasingly important in world trade. For example, a Canadian company supplied Indonesia with railway equipment. Under the countertrade agreement, Indonesia paid for the equipment with timber, rubber, cocoa and textiles. Oil producing countries such as Libya, Nigeria, Iran and Iraq have arranged many countertrade agreements in exchange for crude oil.

QUESTIONS

1 Why is it in the interests of the developed countries that the differences in wealth between themselves and the developing countries do not increase?

2 a) How did the Ivory Coast try to raise the world price of cocoa in 1980?
  b) Why did the price not rise?
  c) What would have happened if it had?

3 a) Copy and complete the table below:

EC tariffs on certain imported goods

Commodity	EC tariff (per cent)
Rice	?
?	13
Crude palm-oil	?
Refined palm-oil	?

  b) Why does the EC place a higher import tariff upon processed goods than on raw materials?

4 a) What is 'countertrade'?
  b) Give examples of countertrade agreements.
  c) What are the advantages of countertrade for developing countries?

5 a) What is OPEC?
  b) On an outline map of the world, shade in and name the OPEC nations shown by their first letter on Figure B. You may use an atlas to help you.
  c) Why do you think OPEC raised oil prices?
  d) What effects did the oil price rises have on developed countries?
  e) Why were the effects of the oil price rises much more serious for the oil importing developing countries?

6 Study Figure C.
  a) What was the price of oil in
    (i) 1960 (ii) 1974 (iii) 1980 (iv) 1987?
  b) Explain the price changes shown on the graph.
  c) Why was OPEC unable to prevent a fall in oil prices during the 1980s?

Figure A shows the remaining colonies of Great Britain. They are the last remnant of a vast empire which once controlled a quarter of the world's population. Political disputes and military conflicts arise over the future of these territories. In 1982, for example, Britain fought a war with Argentina over the Falkland Islands. Peaceful outcomes are possible. Long negotiations with China resulted in an agreement to return Hong Kong to China in 1997.

The Commonwealth

Many of the ex-colonies are now members of the Commonwealth (Figure B). There are 48 members of the Commonwealth, situated in all areas of the world. Forty-two of the member states are developing countries. The Commonwealth is not a formal organization. It is an association of countries that meets every two years in order to discuss matters of interest and general world affairs. Queen Elizabeth II is the Head of State of many of the Commonwealth nations, but this is largely a ceremonial role with little political power.

The Commonwealth is mainly run by the Secretariat based in London. It is responsible for organizing the two-yearly meetings and for circulating information to the Commonwealth nations. The staff of the Secretariat is made up of people from throughout the Commonwealth.

Also based in London is the Commonwealth Fund for Technical Co-operation (CFTC). All member nations of the Commonwealth have to contribute to the CFTC, although the actual amount is up to the nation concerned. In 1986 over £28 million was contributed. The CFTC has concentrated upon developing people's skills rather than funding big projects. It provides:

● technical assistance and training

● encouragement for small-scale agricultural and industrial development

● help in developing export markets

The Commonwealth has been criticized as 'a British-run club', but it also operates on a regional basis. The Canadians and Caribbean member nations meet regularly, as do Australia, India and other Asian members.

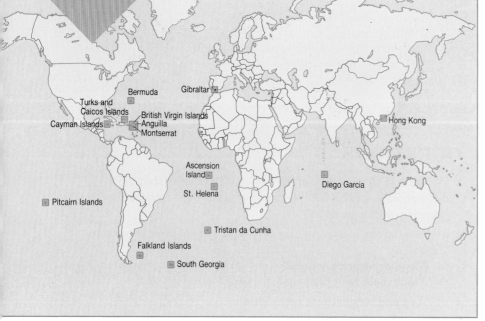

Figure A British colonies

Figure B The Commonwealth

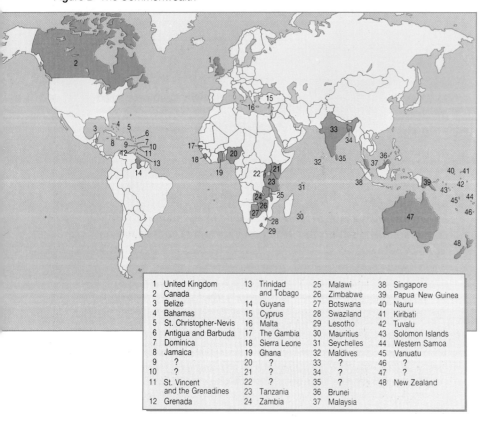

1	United Kingdom	13	Trinidad and Tobago	25	Malawi	38	Singapore
2	Canada	14	Guyana	26	Zimbabwe	39	Papua New Guinea
3	Belize	15	Cyprus	27	Botswana	40	Nauru
4	Bahamas	16	Malta	28	Swaziland	41	Kiribati
5	St. Christopher-Nevis	17	The Gambia	29	Lesotho	42	Tuvalu
6	Antigua and Barbuda	18	Sierra Leone	30	Mauritius	43	Solomon Islands
7	Dominica	19	Ghana	31	Seychelles	44	Western Samoa
8	Jamaica	20	?	32	Maldives	45	Vanuatu
9	?	21	?	33	?	46	?
10	?	22	?	34	?	47	?
11	St. Vincent and the Grenadines	23	Tanzania	35	?	48	New Zealand
12	Grenada	24	Zambia	36	Brunei		
				37	Malaysia		

The European Community

As a member of the EC, Britain has important trade links with many developing countries through the Lomé Convention, in which the Commonwealth Secretary-General played a leading role. The Convention was established in 1975 and has been extended for a five-year period in both 1980 and 1985. The developing countries concerned, mainly ex-colonies of EC nations, receive guaranteed tariff-free entry for their basic exports such as sugar, bananas, rum and beef.

The Lomé Convention has been attacked by those who see it as preserving and even strengthening the old colonial trade links which operated for the benefit of the European nations. It certainly assures the EC of a reliable supply of foodstuffs and raw materials which it cannot produce for itself.

The British Aid Programme

In 1987 Britain gave £1.3 billion worth of aid to developing countries, largely through the Overseas Development Administration (ODA).

Military assistance

Britain maintains military bases in several developing countries including Belize, Brunei and Cyprus. Britain provides military training and sends military advisers to many developing countries throughout the world. This is seen as a way of preserving British influence and encouraging 'friendly' governments.

Sporting and cultural links

These form an important part of Britain's links with the developing world. Cricket tours to and from India, Pakistan, Sri Lanka and the Caribbean countries are a regular and popular feature of the sporting calendar.

Figure C Heads of government at the Vancouver Commonwealth Summit in 1987

Britain has many varied links with the developing world. Perhaps one of the most important is the role of the English language which is one of the most widely spoken languages in the world today. These links work to Britain's advantage as they ensure that Britain maintains an influence on world affairs out of all proportion to the size of its population and economy.

QUESTIONS

1 a) What is the Commonwealth?
b) How many member nations are there?
c) Make a copy of Figure B. Using an atlas to help you, name the countries not named in the key.
d) Name a member nation of the Commonwealth in each of the following continents: Europe, North America, South America, Africa, Asia, Oceania.

2 a) What are the full names of the organizations whose initials are (i) CFTC (ii) ODA?
b) What are the functions of these two organizations?

3 a) What is the Lomé Convention?
b) How has the Convention been criticized?

4 Here is a list of countries where British military advisers have been based during the 1980s: Belize, Mozambique, Zimbabwe, Malawi, Sudan, Saudi Arabia, Oman, Kenya, Kuwait, Zambia and the United Arab Emirates
a) Show these countries on an outline map of the world.
b) What pattern do you notice from the map?
c) Why does Britain provide military assistance to developing countries?

5 a) Make a list of Britain's links with the developing world. Try to include extra links not mentioned on these pages.
b) What are the advantages to Britain of these links?
c) What are the advantages and disadvantages to developing countries of links with a developed country such as Britain?

5.6 Tourism in the developing world

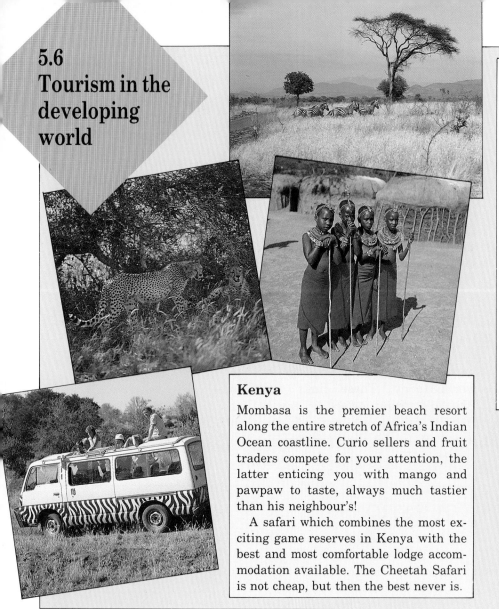

Tanzania

Not until you have stood in the heart of the Serengeti Plains and experienced the feeling of unbelievable space around you, or descended the steep Seneto Hill into the excitement of the Ngorongoro Crater can you possibly realise the spell of Africa – a spell which, once cast, cannot be broken.

Now after many years these legendary names can once again be offered in conjunction with a Safari in Kenya and the opportunity of enjoying Kenya's excellent beach hotels.

The lodges in Tanzania are superbly designed in unique locations, but food, service, maintenance and availability of some commodities are not of the same high standard as in Kenya. The game parks in Tanzania are simply the best and most exciting in the world.

Kenya

Mombasa is the premier beach resort along the entire stretch of Africa's Indian Ocean coastline. Curio sellers and fruit traders compete for your attention, the latter enticing you with mango and pawpaw to taste, always much tastier than his neighbour's!

A safari which combines the most exciting game reserves in Kenya with the best and most comfortable lodge accommodation available. The Cheetah Safari is not cheap, but then the best never is.

Figure A (*above*) The photographs show some of Kenya's tourist attractions. The extracts are from a *Kuoni Holidays* travel brochure

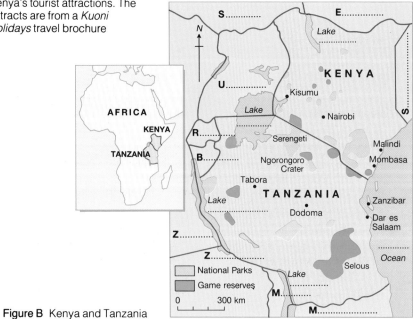

Figure B Kenya and Tanzania

Kenya appears in many tourist brochures. The Kenyan government has made tourist development a priority. It has spent money on building hotels, airports, safari lodges and all the other requirements for tourists from developed countries. The planes landing at Nairobi airport bring rich tourists from Europe, North America and Japan. Some come for Kenya's fine beaches. Most are more interested in the wildlife of East Africa. Lions, cheetahs, elephants and hippopotamuses are among the attractions.

Kenya's tourist industry earns the country over £200 million per year, but tourism does bring problems for a developing country.

- Only 75 per cent of the money spent by tourists stays in Kenya. The rest is taken by the foreign companies which provide the hotels and safaris.
- The tourist drinks Scotch whisky or Russian vodka. The hotels are fitted with American air conditioning and Japanese lifts. The electrical system is Dutch and the fire control system is Italian. The safari vehicles are Japanese Land Cruisers. These imports cost Kenya vital foreign exchange.
- Kenya borrowed money from overseas to pay for the tourist developments, and much of the profits from tourism are spent in repaying the loans.
- In 1983 there were several armed attacks upon tourists. The bad publicity hit Kenya's tourist earnings because people were frightened off. It is risky to become over-dependent upon tourism.

Most of the jobs created for Kenyans are unskilled and poorly paid. Some complain that tourism is a new form of colonialism. Tourism has also come into conflict with Kenya's rapid population growth. More mouths to feed means more demand for farmland. Already some Kenyans are demanding that the National Parks be opened up for farming.

In the past Tanzania chose not to develop tourism, thinking that it took money which could be better used for other purposes. By the early 1980s Tanzania was forced to change its policy. Tourism provides Tanzania's main source of foreign exchange. Loans from the World Bank were used to build new safari lodges and hotels, roads and other tourist-related projects. Now Tanzania wants to build up its tourist industry quickly, while trying to avoid the problems which tourism has brought for Kenya. In 1985 Tanzania attracted only one-fifth the number of tourists that Kenya did, and Tanzania's earnings from tourism were only £30 million.

Figure C Nationality of tourists visiting Kenya

Nationality	Pecentage of total tourists
West German	19
British	12
US	10
Swiss	8
Italian	6
Japanese	3
Canadian	2
Others	40
Total	**100**

QUESTIONS

1 a) Make your own copy of Figure B.
b) Using an atlas, name the countries bordering Kenya and Tanzania.
c) Name the lakes and the ocean.

2 Why are tourists attracted to Kenya for a holiday?

3 What advantages are provided for Kenya by tourism?

4 What problems are created by tourism for a country like Kenya?

5 Figure C shows the nationality of tourists visiting Kenya.
a) Draw a divided bar or pie chart to illustrate these statistics.
b) Why do so many of the tourists visiting Kenya come from Europe, North America and Japan?

6 Study the table below:

The number of tourists visiting Kenya, 1981–86

Year	1981	1982	1983	1984	1985	1986
Tourists (thousands)	352	362	339	298	405	650

a) Describe the changes in the number of tourists shown by the table.
b) What may explain these changes?

7 Study the figures below:

The growth of Kenya's population since 1961

Year	1961	1966	1971	1976	1981	1986
Population (millions)	7.3	9.6	11.9	13.8	17.4	21.1

a) Draw a line graph to illustrate these statistics.
b) In which five year period did the largest population growth occur?
c) What effect might this rapid population growth have upon Kenya's tourist industry?

8 a) What advantages does Tanzania have for tourism?
b) Why has Tanzania chosen in the past not to develop tourism?
c) How did Tanzania afford to build up its tourist industry in recent years?
d) What problem might the loans pose for Tanzania in the future?

Unit 5 ASSESSMENT

1 Study Figure A.
a) Name Cuba's major export commodity. (1 mark)
b) What percentage of Cuba's total exports is made up of this commodity? (2 marks)
c) What problems does a country like Cuba face from this great dependence upon one product for its export earnings? (5 marks)
d) Draw a divided bar to illustrate Cuba's imports. (7 marks)
e) Why does so much of Cuba's import trade consist of
(i) machinery, transport equipment and manufactured goods and
(ii) crude oil and other fuels? (4 marks)

2 a) Add the labels 'raw materials' and 'manufactured goods' in the correct places to show the general pattern of world trade on the following diagram:

(2 marks)
b) (i) Which is of higher value, raw materials or manufactured goods? (1 mark)
(ii) Give reasons for your answer. (3 marks)
c) How did this pattern of trade arise? (3 marks)
d) How do the developed countries benefit from this pattern of trade? (4 marks)

3 a) Draw a sketch map to show the location of Nigeria's major oilfields. (5 marks)
b) Explain how Nigeria benefits from exporting oil. (4 marks)
c) What are the disadvantages to Nigeria of exporting oil? (3 marks)

4 a) What is the Lomé Convention? (4 marks)
b) What are the benefits of the Lomé Convention to
(i) the developing countries and
(ii) the developed countries which have signed it? (4 marks)

5 Study Figure B which shows the country of origin of tourists holidaying in Tunisia.
a) Name the three countries from which the most tourists originated. (3 marks)
b) How many British tourists visited Tunisia? (2 marks)
c) Study the photographs in Figure C and state five attractions which Tunisia has for tourists. (5 marks)
d) Describe the benefits that tourism can bring to a developing country. (6 marks)
e) Explain why the development of tourism can also cause problems. (6 marks)

TOTAL: 75 marks

Figure A Cuba's trade, 1985

Exports	
Commodity	**Percentage of total export earnings**
Sugar & sugar products	?
Minerals	6
Fish and fish products	2
Tobacco & tobacco products	1
Other agricultural products	3
Others	12
Total: £4235 million	**100**

Imports	
Commodity	**Percentage of total import costs**
Crude oil & other fuels	31
Machinery & transport equipment	30
Manufactured goods	17
Food	11
Chemicals	6
Others	5
Total: £5590 million	**100**

Figure B The origin of tourists visiting Tunisia

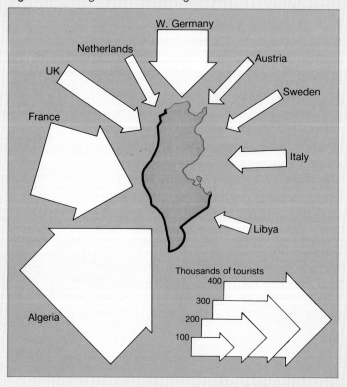

Figure C Some of Tunisia's tourist attractions

Details for pupil profile sheet Unit 5

Knowledge and understanding

1 Developing countries' over-dependence upon exports of primary products
2 Developing countries' debt
3 The pattern of world trade
4 Resource price variations and their effects upon developing countries
5 The market economy; supply and demand
6 OPEC and its role in obtaining higher prices for oil
7 The Brandt Reports
8 Countertrade
9 Britain's relations with the developing world
10 Tourist attractions of developing countries

Skills

1 Drawing divided bars
2 Naming places on a map with the aid of an atlas
3 Preparing a government plan for future development: establishing priorities
4 Draw a line graph
5 Draw a sketch map
6 Interpreting a proportional flow line map
7 Interpreting statistics from a table
8 Empathising with people in a photograph

Values

1 The role of European countries in creating the colonial system of trade
2 The unfair nature of current world trade patterns
3 Effects of tourism upon a developing country

Unit 6: Approaches to development

We talk about the 'developed world' and the 'developing world'. What do we mean? Development means *meeting the needs of people* and *improving society*. **Answer questions 1 to 4** before reading on.

One way of studying how highly developed a country is is to study the Gross National Product (GNP). The GNP measures a country's total production of goods and services – the value of everything a country makes or does in a year. Figure D shows the GNP per person in a number of countries. It is wrong to think that all developing countries have a low GNP. As Figure D shows, some developing countries are among the richest in the world. Their wealth is based upon the resources they possess, especially oil.

GNP is not a particularly good way of measuring development because the needs of people are not simply the need for money. Education, health, justice, peace and self-respect are more important than money.

Figure D GNP per person in selected countries, mid-1980s

Country	GNP per person (pounds Sterling)
Albania	365
Ethiopia	90
Gabon	3070
Greece	2650
Kuwait	12180
Libya	6050
Portugal	1470
Saudi Arabia	8120
Switzerland	10950
United Arab Emirates	15215
UK	6050
USA	9515
World average	**1950**

Figure A A London scene

Figure B (*above*) A Liverpool scene

Figure C (*left*) A Brazilian family

Figure E

Figure H

Figure F

Figure G

QUESTIONS

1 a) Write a list of the *basic needs* of people for survival.
b) Share your list with your neighbour and prepare a joint list of basic needs.

2 a) Make a list of all the electrical machines that are in your house. Group them under the following headings: Toys, Entertainment, Comfort, Kitchen, Others.
b) Which two groups had the most items of electrical equipment from your list?
c) How many items from your list do you think are essential to your life?

3 Write a list of ways in which you could measure the level of development of a country. Here is one to start your list: the percentage of the workforce which is unemployed.

4 Study the photographs (Figures A to C).
What could be done to improve the standard of living of the people in each of the photographs?

5 What is GNP?

6 a) Name the five nations with the highest GNPs per person in Figure D.
b) Which of these countries could be called 'developed' and which 'developing'?

7 Study the views in Figures E to H. Which of the photographs show scenes from the developing world? Make a copy of the table below and complete it:

Figure	Developed or developing country?	Reasons for choice
E		
F		
G		
H		

8 After completing Question 7, turn to page 123 where you will find the answers at the bottom of the page.
a) How many of the four photographs did you place correctly?
b) Can you draw any conclusions from this exercise?

113

6.2
A development index

How do we measure development? On the previous page we saw that wealth, in terms of GNP, is not by itself a good way of measuring development. Other factors must be taken into account.

Figure A gives a range of information about ten countries. This information can be used to work out a simple development index.

Figure A Measures of development for ten countries

	UK	USA	India	Ghana	Tanzania	Burkina Faso	Bolivia	Saudi Arabia	Indonesia	Portugal
Birth rate (per thousand)	13	16	34	47	51	49	48	46	36	18
Death rate (per thousand)	12	9	11	16	17	24	18	13	15	10
Life expectancy (years)	74	75	53	52	50	42	51	59	54	71
Infant mortality (per thousand)	10	9	118	107	96	152	124	103	85	30
Population per doctor	650	520	3700	7200	17800	48900	2100	1400	11500	540
Urban population (per cent of total population)	92	80	24	40	15	10	36	75	25	34
Percentage of workforce in farming	2	3	60	48	78	80	49	58	56	24
Fertilizer used (kg/ha)	140	46	37	3	1	0.1	0.2	2	47	57
Literacy rate (percentage of adults)	99	99	40	42	72	12	60	30	70	97
GNP per capita ($)	9110	14100	260	320	240	180	510	12200	560	2200
Annual inflation rate (per cent)	6	4	6	11	36	7	11750	0	5	20
Daily calorie intake per person	3210	3630	2130	1520	2410	1900	2115	3005	2400	3000
Televisions (per thousand)	320	580	1	3	0	0	1	220	150	210
Cars (per thousand)	282	522	1	8	2	2	1	14	5	132
Tractors (per thousand)	10	19	1	0	1	0	0	0	0	8
Telephones (per thousand)	492	770	4	5	3	1	8	77	6	143
Energy use per person (kg of coal equivalent)	4700	9300	230	95	40	30	350	3600	240	1330

QUESTIONS

1 On an outline map of the world shade in the countries listed in Figure A.

2 Copy the table below.

3 The figures for GNP per capita in Figure A have been ranked in the first column of the table below. Rank 1 is given to the country with the highest GNP per capita. For each of the other four measures of development in the table, rank the countries. Rank 1 should be given to the highest level of development in each case: the lowest birth rate, the highest life expectancy, the highest number of cars and the highest energy use.

4 For each country, add up the five ranks and write the total in the **Total** column. This figure is the development index.

5 a) Rank the totals, with the lowest total rank 1.
b) On the world map which you used for Question 1, number the ten countries according to their ranks.
c) Name the countries ranked 1, 2 and 3.
d) Name the countries ranked 8, 9 and 10.

6 a) Now repeat the exercise, using the following measures of development: (i) death rate (ii) population per doctor (iii) urban population (iv) daily calorie intake per person (v) one other measure chosen from Figure A.
b) How did the development index rank order vary between the two exercises?
c) Explain the differences.

7 How effective is this method as a means of measuring development?

Table for working out a development index

Country	GNP per capita	Birth rate	Life expectancy	Cars	Energy use	Total	Rank order
UK	3						
USA	1						
India	8						
Ghana	7						
Tanzania	9						
Burkina Faso	10						
Bolivia	6						
Saudi Arabia	2						
Indonesia	5						
Portugal	4						

World map

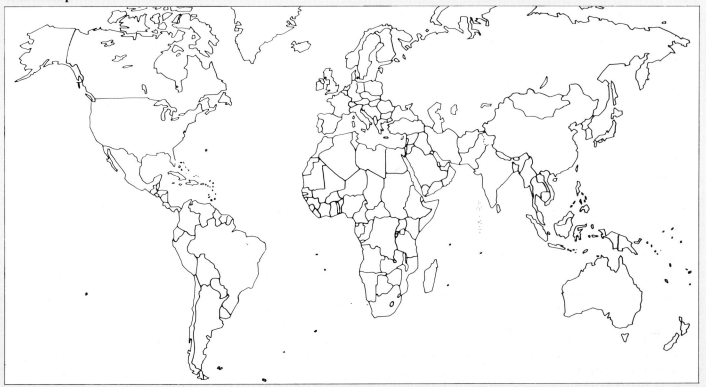

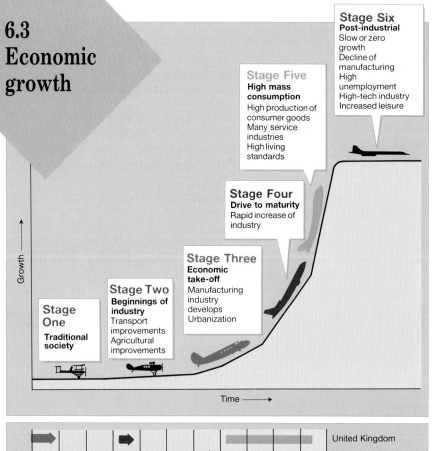

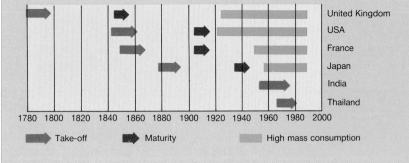

Figure A (*top*) Rostow's Growth Model

Figure B (*above*) Times at which selected countries entered the different stages of Rostow's Growth Model

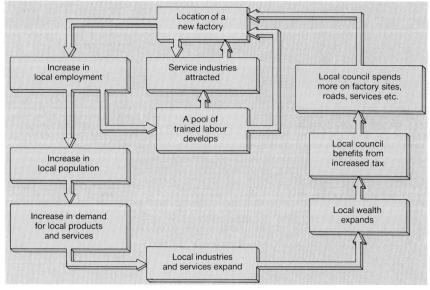

Figure C Myrdal's Model – the 'multiplier effect'

Why do some countries have a higher level of development than others? Can less developed countries follow the same course to become more highly developed? Economists have sought answers to these questions.

Rostow's Growth Model

In 1960 the US economist Rostow said that developed countries had passed through a series of stages of development. At each stage the wealth of the country increased as factories and service industries replaced agriculture and craft industries. He compared the stages of development to the flight of an aircraft (Figure A).

Figure B shows when several developed countries entered the different stages of the Growth Model. Rostow claimed that the poor, developing countries could follow the same course to development. This was widely accepted during the 1960s and many of the development programmes adopted by developing countries aimed to develop economic take-off by building large-scale industrial projects.

In recent years the idea that developing countries can pass through the stages of Rostow's Growth Model has been heavily criticized. The model is based on the development of the Western industrial nations. It is very unlikely that developing countries can follow this course because:

● Today's developed countries were able to take the resources of the whole world, much of it through their empires. They built up power and wealth which makes it impossible for developing countries to compete.

● Developed countries ensure that there can be no large-scale development of manufacturing in developing countries by charging tariffs on imports of manufactured goods.

New theories of economic development stress that the developed countries became wealthy by exploiting the people and resources of Africa, Asia and Latin America. The developed countries continue to exploit these areas through *neo-colonialism*, and this ensures that the developing countries cannot become developed.

Those who still support Rostow point to the success of some developing countries such as South Korea and Singapore, the so-called Newly Industrialized Countries. They claim that the NICs have passed through Stage Three and on into Stage Four. It remains to be seen whether they will achieve Stage Five.

A Sixth Stage has been added to Rostow's model which takes account of the decline of manufacturing industry in several developed countries. The Sixth Stage assumes that the aircraft has reached cruising height and that future growth will be slow.

Myrdal's Model

Myrdal, a Swedish economist, developed a model theory to explain the pattern of economic development. This is shown in simplified form in Figure C for the effects resulting from the opening of a new factory. It could also apply to the development of a new resource or raw material. Once begun, the area attracts money, industry and people: an industrial region develops. This 'snowballing' of growth is called the 'multiplier effect'.

Myrdal realized that a region developed at the expense of other regions. On a large scale, Myrdal's model can be applied to Western Europe growing at the expense of the Third World. Myrdal said that there would eventually be a spread of development outside the region because of the effects of congestion.

Friedmann's Core-Periphery Model

Friedmann looked at the geographical differences in development (Figure D). He identified a core, an upward transition and a downward transition region.

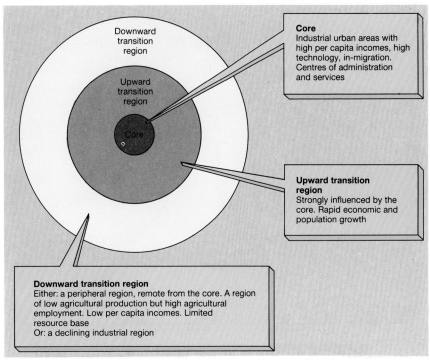

Core
Industrial urban areas with high per capita incomes, high technology, in-migration. Centres of administration and services

Upward transition region
Strongly influenced by the core. Rapid economic and population growth

Downward transition region
Either: a peripheral region, remote from the core. A region of low agricultural production but high agricultural employment. Low per capita incomes. Limited resource base
Or: a declining industrial region

Figure D Friedmann's Core-Periphery Model

Ways forward

There is still no widely-accepted theory explaining economic growth. Countries have adopted different approaches. Some countries have been more successful than others.

QUESTIONS

1 a) Copy Figure A.
  b) What increases in each of the stages of Rostow's Growth Model?

2 Study Figure B.
  a) When did the UK enter (i) Stage Three (ii) Stage Four (iii) Stage Five of the Growth Model?
  b) Which of the countries shown in Figure B reached Stage Five first?
  c) Which of the countries passed through Stage Four most quickly?

3 a) Why is it unlikely that developing countries will pass through the stages of Rostow's Growth Model?
  b) How do the following countries fit into Rostow's Growth Model:
    (i) Newly Industrialized Countries such as South Korea and Singapore?
    (ii) Oil-rich countries such as Saudi Arabia and Kuwait?

4 a) What do you understand by 'the multiplier effect'?
  b) What is Myrdal's 'spread effect'?

5 a) Describe Friedmann's Core-Periphery Model.
  b) Consider the levels of development in the regions of a country such as Brazil or Nigeria. How far can the core and periphery regions of the Friedmann model be recognized?

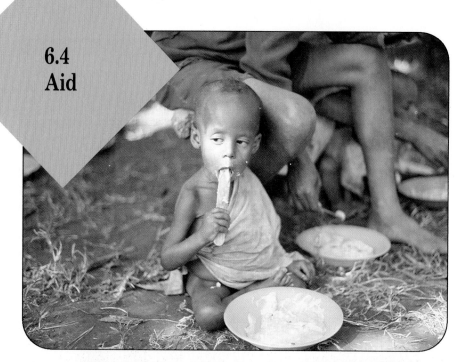

The developed world, with 25 per cent of the world's population, has 80 per cent of the world's wealth. This is clearly brought home to people in developed countries through tragic pictures on their television screens (like Figure A, or far worse). Such dreadful scenes make many people angry: why are people allowed to starve while elsewhere in the world food is stored or thrown away for lack of demand? Can't something be done to end the suffering?

Figure A (*photograph, left*) A victim of famine. But this child, eating food aid provided by Oxfam, is probably luckier than many

OXFAM AIRLIFT TO VICTIMS IN MOZAMBIQUE

The agony in Mozambique continues. South African backed bandit forces are still brutally terrorizing whole communities.

Niassa province in the north is very badly hit. Over 100, 000 people have fled their homes in terror. Virtually everyone lacks basic necessities such as clothes, soap, sugar and oil.

Since this time last year Oxfam has responded by airlifting 1, 000 tons of emergency supplies to those in greatest need.

Now Oxfam is urgently helping 24, 000 destitute families that are settling in safer areas.

Just £12 from you could buy enough tools for 2 displaced families to grow their own food.

Working with the Mozambique Government Oxfam is providing emergency rations, clothing and vital seeds and tools to grow food. Many supplies will again have to be flown in by emergency airlift.

PEOPLE IN MOZAMBIQUE NEED YOUR HELP

Figure B An Oxfam relief appeal advertisement

Charity

One response to the television pictures of starving people is to send money to a charity which helps the developing world. Oxfam, Band Aid, Save the Children Fund, the Red Cross, the Red Crescent and Christian Aid are important charities working in developing countries. They spend their money on small-scale development projects such as local water supplies, craft industries and farm improvements. They also help with health and education. Emergency aid is a vital part of their work; Oxfam puts aside some of its income for un-budgeted emergencies such as hurricanes or floods.

Official aid

Charities do very important work, but their contribution amounts to only about 5 per cent of the total aid going to developing countries. Most of the aid comes from the government of one country sending aid to the government of another. This is called *bilateral aid*. Most of the rest goes through international organizations such as the United Nations and the European Community. This is called *multilateral aid*.

Official aid tends to concentrate upon the following:

- big projects such as dams, power stations, highways, airports and sea ports. These are intended to provide a boost for the developing countries' economies and to improve trade
- the supply of manufactured goods
- financial aid in the form of loans or grants
- food aid

There is an important difference between 'crisis aid' and 'long-term development aid'. Crisis aid aims to keep people alive during an emergency. Food supplies and medicines are rushed to disaster areas. Tents and blankets may also be needed. Such efforts are short-term responses to an emergency.

Long-term development aid aims to improve standards of living in order to *prevent* future food emergencies. 'Give a person a meal and you feed them for a day. Teach a person to farm and they will feed themselves for life.'

The benefits of aid

Aid does not always reach the people it is aimed at. It often helps the rich in a developing country to get richer, rather than helping the poor. For example, the wealthy landowners make money from new irrigation projects, not the poor farmworkers. It is also claimed that large amounts of aid money have been stolen by corrupt officials.

Even if aid does reach the people it is aimed at, the results of receiving the aid may not be favourable. The import of free food into a developing country can put local farmers out of business by forcing down food prices. A second example is provided by the supply of farm machinery which puts poor farmworkers out of their jobs and requires costly spare parts to be imported.

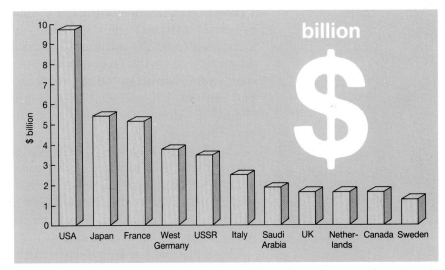

Figure C The main aid-giving nations

Figure D Collecting for Christian Aid

QUESTIONS

1 a) Name five major charities providing aid to the developing world.
   b) What percentage of total aid is provided by charities?

2 a) What does Figure B show?
   b) What impression does the advertisement give you of conditions in the country?
   c) Why did Oxfam choose that photograph for the appeal poster?

3 What is the difference between (a) bilateral aid and multilateral aid (b) crisis aid and long-term development aid?

4 How does the aid work of charities tend to differ from official aid work?

5 a) Study Figure C and name the five nations giving most aid.
   b) How much aid did the UK give?
   c) How has aid been criticized?

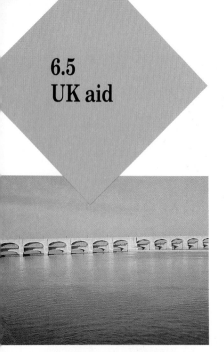

6.5 UK aid

In 1987 UK charities sent £130 million overseas. Official government aid amounted to £1300 million. The aid is administered by the Overseas Development Administration (ODA). Sixty-two per cent of UK aid is bilateral aid. Figure E shows the main areas of spending.

The Brandt Report of 1980 stated that 0.7 per cent of a developed country's GNP should be given in overseas aid. Figure C shows that Britain fails to achieve even half that figure whilst many countries have exceeded it.

There has been a long debate in the UK about the real purpose of aid. There are two points of view:

● Some believe that aid should be used to help the poor in the world's poorest nations.

● Others see aid as a means of boosting British industry by supplying manufactured goods to developing countries.

Some aid deals have clearly been designed to help British industry rather than the poor. The £60 million sale of Westland helicopters to India in 1986 was intended to keep the ailing British company in business. A previous deal in

Figure A (top) The Sukkur Barrage, Pakistan
Figure B (above) The Mrica Dam under construction, Indonesia

1978 demonstrates the mistakes that can be made. Aid funds were used to pay for fifty British Leyland buses for Zambia. Not designed to cope with Zambia's rough roads, they soon broke down. No money was available for repairs or maintenance. A short-sighted policy to support British industry had resulted in a great waste of money.

An increasing part of British aid is Aid and Trade Provision (ATP). The ODA says 'ATP finance helps British firms to compete on an equal footing with companies from other developed countries when they are trying to win contracts for projects in developing countries'. Critics say that this money should not come from the hard-pressed aid budget, but from other sources.

Case studies of UK aid

The Sukkur Barrage. In 1932 a barrage was built across the River Indus at Sukkur in Pakistan. It was part of an irrigation scheme for an area which now produces cotton, wheat, rice and sugar cane. Its future was threatened by increasing salt content of the water. The UK has contributed £28 million towards reducing the salt content and improving crop yields. A further £9.4 million is being used to repair and modernize the Barrage, ensuring the continued protection of over 3 million hectares of vital farmland.

The Mrica Dam. A joint UK–Swedish group of companies is building a hydro-electric dam on the Serayu River in central Java, Indonesia. The dam is intended to encourage industrial development in the region. The scheme will cost £321 million of which £12 million has been provided through Aid and Trade Provision.

Woodlands in Lesotho. UK aid is being used in a long-term project to plant trees in Lesotho. The country is now virtually treeless. The project has been under way since 1973. It aims to provide fuelwood and timber, and to reduce soil erosion. It is hoped that the

Figure C Aid as a percentage of donor GNP for selected countries, 1986

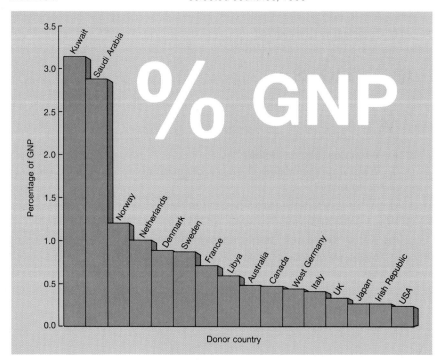

woodlands will eventually cover a large area. At present it is concentrating on developing tree nurseries and planting areas of between 20 and 200 hectares around lowland villages where most people live and where the demand for wood is highest.

Immunization. In 1987 £5 million of UK aid was given to UNICEF (United Nations Children's Fund) to support its immunization programme in China, Zimbabwe, Zambia, Lesotho and Botswana. In 1970 only 5 per cent of the children in these countries were immunized against killer diseases such as diphtheria, whooping cough and tetanus. Today the figure is 40 per cent.

Despite some spectacular failures, UK aid is largely successful. Eighty per cent of the money spent goes to the world's poorest countries. Careful monitoring ensures that at least some of the money actually benefits the poorest people at whom it is aimed. The major criticism remains that the total amount of UK aid is too low when compared with other developed countries.

Figure D Extract from *British Aid* (ODA 1987)

The aims of the UK aid programme

Two-thirds of the world's population live in poverty. Development aid is a practical way for wealthy countries to help poorer countries to:

- give their people a higher standard of living
- make better use of their land and natural resources
- preserve their environment
- improve their health and education services.

We give aid because there is a moral case for doing so: too many nations are suffering from disease, poverty and an uncertain future. We are more fortunate.

But it is also in our own interest to give aid. There are political and commercial reasons why we should do so. Nations rely upon each other more than ever before.

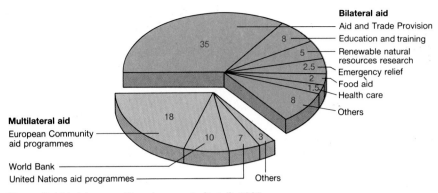

Figure E UK aid expenditure (per cent of total), 1985

QUESTIONS

1 What percentage of total UK aid in 1987 was provided by (a) charities and (b) official government aid?

2 Study Figure E.
a) What was the amount of (i) bilateral aid (ii) multilateral aid in 1987?
b) What were the two largest sectors of bilateral aid?
c) Where were the three largest contributions of multilateral aid made in 1985?

3 a) What percentage of a country's GNP did the Brandt Report state should be given in overseas aid?
b) Study Figure C and name the countries which exceeded this percentage in 1986.
c) What percentage of the UK's GNP was spent on aid?

4 What are the two conflicting viewpoints about the real purpose of UK aid?

5 a) What is Aid and Trade Provision?
b) How has ATP been criticized?

6 Study the table below:

Countries receiving most bilateral aid from the UK in 1986

Country	Percentage of total UK bilateral aid	Country	Percentage of total UK bilateral aid
India	13	Ethiopia	4
Sudan	5	Zambia	3
Bangladesh	5	Zimbabwe	3
Kenya	4	Egypt	2
Indonesia	4	Tanzania	2

a) Using an atlas to help you, shade in these countries on an outline map of the world.
b) UK aid has been criticized by some people for concentrating too much on the Commonwealth. How many of the countries in the table are members of the Commonwealth. Figure B on page 106 can help you answer this.
c) What does Figure D say are the aims of the UK aid programme?
d) What are the two reasons in the extract for giving aid?

Unit 6 ASSESSMENT

1 Study the graphs below (Figure A) which give information on the levels of development of five countries.

Figure A

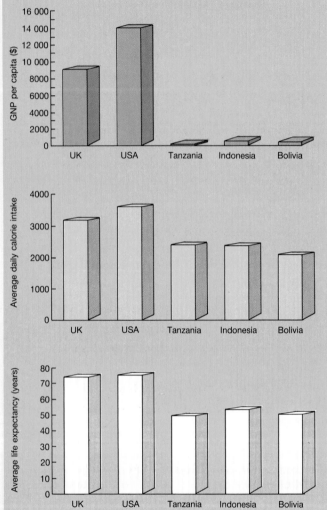

a) What do the letters GNP stand for? (1 mark)

b) What does 'per capita' mean? (1 mark)

c) Which country has the lowest GNP per capita? (1 mark)

d) Which country has the lowest daily calorie intake per capita? (1 mark)

e) Which of the five countries are in the developing world? (1 mark)

f) Use the graphs to state the basic differences shown between the countries in the developing world and those in the developed world. (3 marks)

g) Give two other ways of measuring the level of development in a country and explain why each is considered to be a useful indicator of development. (6 marks)

2 Even in the poorest countries there are great differences in the level of development of the people.

a) Name a developing country that you have studied where there is a great difference in the level of develoment of the people. (1 mark)

b) Explain why some of the people who live in that country are able to have a high standard of living. (3 marks)

c) How could the wealth of that country be shared out more evenly amongst the people? (3 marks)

3 a) Name three major charities which help developing countries. (3 marks)

b) (i) What is meant by crisis aid? (1 mark)

(ii) Name three types of crisis aid. (3 marks)

c) How can long-term aid schemes be used to help people provide for themselves? (3 marks)

d) Explain why aid schemes do not always benefit the people whose need is greatest. (4 marks)

e) What are the benefits to a developed country of sending overseas aid to help developing countries? (4 marks)

4 Imagine that you are the President of a poor African country. A developed country has offered you various aid packages:

(1) A squadron of fighter aircraft for your air force.

(2) A vehicle assembly factory, providing you agree to assemble vehicles made in the donor country.

(3) Six training aircraft and six transport aircraft for your air force.

(4) One hundred schoolteachers from the donor country.

(5) Fifty doctors and fifty nurses from the donor country.

(6) Five mobile clinics and a medical school to train the local staff.

(7) Port improvements and two cargo ships.

(8) A factory processing your country's agricultural products, provided you agree to sell the products at a cheap rate to the donor country.

a) Read through the eight aid packages.

(i) Think of the situation in your country and then place the packages in rank order with the one which you would find most useful at the top of your order.

(ii) For the top two and bottom two packages in your order explain why you placed them in those positions. (8 marks)

b) For your top two packages say what might be the disadvantages of accepting even these aid packages. (4 marks)

5 a) Copy and complete the diagram of Rostow's Model of Economic Growth (Figure B). (5 marks)

b) How has the model been criticized? (4 marks)

c) Copy Figure C and choose the correct label to write in the empty boxes. (5 marks)

TOTAL: 65 marks

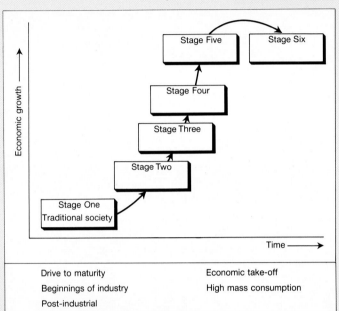

Figure B Rostow's Model of Economic Growth

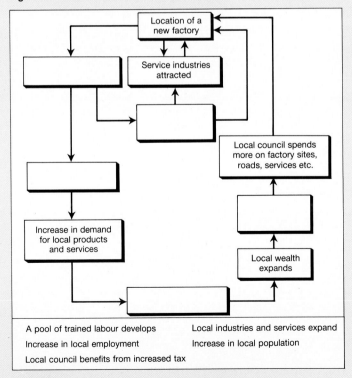

Figure C Myrdal's Model – the 'multiplier effect'

Answers to Question 7 on page 112:

Figure E Developed country (a Greek peasant farmer)

Figure F Developing country (Harare, Zimbabwe)

Figure G Developed country (an Italian woman)

Figure H Developing country (Caracas Airport, Venezuela)

Index

A
Aid 118
Australia: Snowy Mountains 82

B
Bolivia: tin mining 33
Brandt Commission 105
Brazil: Drought Polygon 84
　　　 Forestry 18, 28
　　　 hydro-electricity 58, 84

C
Charity 118
Chernobyl nuclear disaster 62
Coal 38–43, 54
Cod War 24
Commonwealth 106
Cornwall 32, 34, 71
Countertrade 105
Cuba 110

D
Deforestation: Brazil 18, 28
　　　　　　　 Ivory Coast 16
　　　　　　　 UK 14

E
Ecosystem 94
Electricity 56–57
　 fossil-fuelled 56
　 geothermal 70
　 hydro 58, 83, 84
　 national grid 57
　 nuclear 60–63, 72
　 solar 68
　 tidal 64
　 wind power 66
European Community (EC):
　 Common Fishing Policy 26
　 Lomé Convention 107
　 Regional Development Fund 80

F
Fishing 20–27, 37
Fish farming 23
Forestry 10–19
Forestry Commission 14
France: nuclear power 63
　　　　 tidal power 64
Friedmann's Core-Periphery
　 Model 117

G
Gas 54
Geothermal power 70
Grimsby 24
Gross National Product (GNP) 112,
　 114
Gulf War 8, 45

H
Hinkley Point 72
Hull 24, 29
Humberside: fishing 24
Hydro-electricity 58, 83, 84
Hydrological cycle 76

I
Iceland: fishing 24
　　　　 geothermal power 70
India 99
Inland waterways 86–89
　 in Netherlands 86
　 in Switzerland 86
　 in UK 88, 94
　 in West Germany 86
Iron ore 36
Irrigation 82, 96
Itaipu hydro-electric scheme 58
Italy: geothermal power 70
Ivory Coast 16

J

K
Kaolin 34
Kenya: tourism 108
Kielder Forest 14, 80
Kielder Water 80

L
London: groundwater supplies 77,
　 97

M
Malaysia: tin mining 32, 103
Mauritania: fishing 37
　　　　　　 iron ore 37
Mersey Barrage 65
Minerals 30
Mining 30–51
　 methods 30
Mozambique 118
Myrdal's Multiplier Effect
　 Model 116

N
Netherlands: inland waterways 87
　　　　　　 River Rhine 92
Nigeria 100
Northumberland 14, 80
Norfolk Broads 94
Norway: fishing 22
Nuclear power 60–63, 72, 75
　 in France 63
　 in UK 60, 72
　 in USSR 62

O
Oil 44–49, 51, 55, 100, 104
OPEC 104
Over-fishing 6, 22, 26

P
Paraguay: hydro-electricity 59
Persian (Arabian) Gulf 8, 45, 46

Q

R
Recycling 7
Reserves 7
Resources: definition 4
　　　　　 non-renewable 6
　　　　　 renewable 6, 12
Rhine, River 86, 92
Rostow's Growth Model 116

S
Saudi Arabia: agriculture 47
　　　　　　　 industry 47
　　　　　　　 oil 46
Severn Barrage 64
Severn, River 89
Solar heating 69
Solar power 68
Southampton 71
Switzerland: inland waterways 86

T
Tanzania 98, 108
Tidal power 64
Tin mining: Bolivia 33
　　　　　　 Malaysia 32
　　　　　　 UK 32
Tunisia: tourism 110

U
United Nations: Law of the Sea 27
USA: Central Valley of
　 California 96
USSR: Chernobyl nuclear
　 disaster 62

V

W
Water pollution 90, 92
Water supply 79
West Germany: coal-mining 38
　 inland waterways 87
　 River Rhine 92
Wind power 66

Acknowledgements

The publishers and author would like to thank the following people for their permission to use copyright material:

AeroCamera – p. 97; Aspect Picture Library – p. 60, /J. Alex Langley p. 30 (*middle*), /Peter Carmichael p. 33 (*right*), /Chris Schwarz p. 112 (*right*); Australia House – p. 83 (*right*); Australian News & Information Bureau – p. 82; Herbert Ballard – p. 25 (*right*); Blakes (Norfolk Broads Holiday) Ltd. – p. 94; British Airways – p. 5 (*top right*); British Coal – p. 5 (*top left*), 31 (*top right*), 42; British Petroleum – p. 5 (*centre left*), 104 (*bottom left*); Camera Press – David Rubinger p. 104 (*top left*), /Don Robertson p. 32; J. Allan Cash Ltd. – p. 4 (*left*), 30 (*top*), 46, 55, 58, 112 (*top left*), 120 (*top*); CEGB – p. 56 (*bottom*), 61 (*top right*), 75; Cine Photo Productions Ltd. – p. 120 (*bottom*); Commonwealth Secretariat – p. 107; Compix – p. 49; Creative Company – p. 69 (*right*); Crown Copyright – p. 45; De Beers Consolidated Mines – p. 48; Michael Dixon – p. 111 (*top and 2nd from top*); Patrick Eagar – p. 78; English China Clays – p. 34, 35; Flight Refuelling Ltd – p. 26; Forestry Commission – p. 14; Nance Fyson – p. 7, 119; Gannaway P. R. – p. 111 (*2nd from bottom and bottom*); John Hillelson Agency – p. 9; Hull Daily Mail – p. 25 (*left*); Hulton Picture Company – p. 54; Hutchison Library – p. 16, 17, 101 (*left*), /Nancy Durrell McKenna p. 4 (*top right*), /Sarah Errington p. 112 (*bottom left*), /B. Gerard p. 11, /Richard House p. 84, /Juliet Highet Brimah p. 113 (*centre left*), /K. E. Job p. 31 (*top left*), /Anna Tully p. 101 (*right*); IDG/Aerophoto Teuge – p. 86 (*top*); Inter Nationes – p. 86 (*centre right*), 92; Lupe Cunha – p. 85; Magnum – Bruno Barbey p. 113 (*bottom left*), /F. Scianna p. 33 (*left*), /Guy Le Querrec p. 36 (*left, right*); Sir Robert McAlpine & Sons Ltd – p. 64 (*bottom*); Archie Miles – p. 40; Mittet Foto – Pål Bugge p. 23; Tony Morrison – p. 19, 59; Nestlé – p. 104 (*centre top*); Northumbrian Water/Airfotos – p. 80; Nuclear Electricity Information Group – p. 61 (*centre right*); OXFAM – p. 118 (*top*), / Jenny Matthews p. 118 (*bottom*); Pan Publishers – p. 104 (*top right*); Paul Popper Ltd – p. 24; Photobank – /Peter Baker p. 108 (*top left, bottom left, centre*); Picturepoint – p. 98; Neil Punnett – p. 70 (*top*), 88 (*centre right, bottom right, left*), 102, 113 (*top left*); RAE, Farnborough – p. 76; RAG-Foto – p. 38; Rapho – p. 64 (*top*); Royal Mint – p. 30 (*bottom*; Science Photo Library – /Martin Bond p. 69 (*left*), /Jerry Mason p. 90, /Tom McHugh p. 67; Southern Media Services – p. 83 (*left*); Spectrum Colour Library – p. 47, 63, 68, 108 (*right*), /Keith Jones p. 108 (*top centre*); Swiss National Tourist Office – p. 86 (*centre left*); Charles Tait – p. 66 (*top*); Topham Picture Library – p. 22, 62; Water Library Visual Resource Loan – p. 5 (*centre right*); West Air Photography – p. 50, 91; Zefa Picture Library – p. 20, /W. F. Davidson p. 5 (*bottom left*), /Hunter p. 31 (*top middle*), /T. Ives p. 56 (*top*), /Paolo Koch p. 70 (*bottom*), /Reichwein p. 4 (*bottom right*), /H. Strass p. 113 (*right*), /Simon Warner p. 88 (*top right*).

The cover photograph is reproduced by permission of Zefa Picture Library.

The illustrations are by Oxford Illustrators, Vanessa Luff and Terry McKivragan/Linda Rogers Associates.

Pupil Profile Sheet
Resources, Energy and Development

Unit ☐

Pupil name _____

After completing this unit you should be able to do the following:

KNOWLEDGE AND UNDERSTANDING
Understand and use the following terms and concepts:

	YES	NO
1 _____		
2 _____		
3 _____		
4 _____		
5 _____		
6 _____		
7 _____		
8 _____		
9 _____		
10 _____		

SKILLS
Understand and use the following skills:

1 _____		
2 _____		
3 _____		
4 _____		
5 _____		
6 _____		
7 _____		
8 _____		
9 _____		
10 _____		

VALUES

1 _____		
2 _____		
3 _____		